Mensa
The High IQ Society

LOGIC TESTS

THIS IS A CARLTON BOOK

This edition published in 2016 by
Carlton Books
20 Mortimer Street
London W1T 3JW

ISBN: 978-1-78097-516-0

All images: © iStockphoto & Shutterstock

Printed in China

Mensa
The High IQ Society

LOGIC TESTS

CHALLENGE YOUR POWERS OF DEDUCTION AND LOGICAL THINKING WITH OVER 200 PUZZLES

Tim Dedopulos

CARLTON
BOOKS

What is Mensa

Mensa is the international society for people with a high IQ.
We have more than 100,000 members in over 40 countries worldwide.

The society's aims are:
   to identify and foster human intelligence for the benefit of humanity
   to encourage research in the nature, characteristics, and uses of intelligence
   to provide a stimulating intellectual and social environment for its members

Anyone with an IQ score in the top two per cent of population is eligible to become a member of Mensa – are you the 'one in 50' we've been looking for?

Mensa membership offers an excellent range of benefits:
   Networking and social activities nationally and around the world
   Special Interest Groups – hundreds of chances to pursue your hobbies
    and interests – from art to zoology!
   Monthly members' magazine and regional newsletters
   Local meetings – from games challenges to food and drink
   National and international weekend gatherings and conferences
   Intellectually stimulating lectures and seminars
   Access to the worldwide SIGHT network for travellers and hosts

For more information about Mensa: www.mensa.org, or

British Mensa Ltd.,
St John's House,
St John's Square,
Wolverhampton
WV2 4AH
Telephone: +44 (0) 1902 772771
E-mail: services@mensa.org.uk
www.mensa.org.uk

Contents

INTRODUCTION   6

THE PUZZLES   7

THE ANSWERS   129

INTRODUCTION

Welcome to Mensa's Logic Tests – and to 200 logical puzzles of every conceivable variety. Inside, you'll find mental problems to test your powers of reasoning to the limit. Even the toughest puzzlers will find themselves scratching their heads from time to time. But then, this is Mensa, the world's foremost High IQ society. What else were you expecting?

Puzzles have been a cornerstone of human society for as long as such a thing has existed. From every corner of the Earth, from every era of history that we have more than fragments from, we have evidence of puzzles. Some of the earliest bits of writing we've found are maths puzzles inscribed into clay tablets. The urge to solve puzzles is hard-wired into us.

It's no surprise really, when you think about it. We're a curious species. Our intelligence and imagination have brought us the modern world. If we didn't like to experiment and find answers to the things that were puzzling us, humanity as we know it would not exist. Our physical adaptability is important, but it is our mental flexibility – the ability to ask "what if?" – that really defines us.

Our capacity for logical analysis – for reason – is one of the greatest tools in our mental arsenal, on a par with creativity and lateral induction. Logic is the very backbone of our scientific method, and despite our everyday assumptions, it is not necessarily obvious. When obvious event A always causes obvious event B, the link is clear to all, even birds and animals. But looking at A and B and asking why the one inevitably brings the other is a

relatively recent development, even in terms of human history. This is the very core of scientific thought, of reason itself.

The human brain gives meaning and structure to the world through analysis, pattern recognition, and logical deduction. We understand our sense input by categorising things, and looking at what those categories imply. The more accurate our mental models, our categories, the better our understanding of the world. Our urge to measure and test ourselves is an unavoidable reflex that results from that drive for greater understanding. So what could be more natural than spending time puzzling?

The logic puzzles contained within this book will definitely let you put your brain to the test. There's no guesswork required, but that isn't to say that you won't need to do a little work for the answers. A core method of the scientific process is to form theories from the data, and test them against the evidence. When your theory is contradicted, you go back to the drawing board. In this book, all the data is in front of you. All you have to do is piece it together.

Humans get a very pleasurable sense of achievement from succeeding at things, particularly when we suspect they might be too hard for us. Let's be clear – solving these puzzles won't be easy. But it will be fun.

Happy puzzling.

THE PUZZLES

01 Can you divide up this board to correctly show the 28 dominoes listed below?

2	0	0	6	5	3	3	0
3	6	5	4	0	1	1	3
2	0	2	2	4	5	3	6
4	6	5	5	2	5	5	0
2	2	1	0	4	0	6	3
6	6	3	4	4	2	1	5
4	1	3	1	4	6	1	1

0	0

0	1	1	1

0	2	1	2	2	2

0	3	1	3	2	3	3	3

0	4	1	4	2	4	3	4	4	4

0	5	1	5	2	5	3	5	4	5	5	5

0	6	1	6	2	6	3	6	4	6	5	6	6	6

8

Answer see page 130

Answer see page 130

02 Can you match the fragments to reassemble the names of several Hollywood celebrities?

MC	MIN	IGAN	HANN
GEL	JU	DRI	TORN
THEW	OW	VER	NIE
DREY	AN	LIA	FUS
WIL	ERL	KIE	INA
UGHEY	SUTH	SON	GIB
LIE	SON	SON	ALY
JO	CONA	AND	MEL
EN	FER	RIP	MAT

Following this set of simple instructions is supposed to help you cross the road safely. There is an error, and if you follow them exactly, you might never cross the road. What is the problem?

1. Walk to the pavement where you want to cross.
2. Face the direction that you want to cross in.
3. Look both ways, and remember if you see any vehicles.
4. Are there any vehicles within 75ft? If yes, go back to 2, else proceed.
5. Walk across the road briskly.
6. Get onto the pavement in front of you.
7. Stop.

Answer see page 130

Can you insert the mathematical operators + – * / ( ) to make these equations valid?

Answer see page 130

A 7 ◯ 6 ◯ 5 ◯ 15 ◯ 18 = 23

B 9 ◯ 7 ◯ 7 ◯ 3 ◯ 13 = 13

C 8 ◯ 9 ◯ 12 ◯ 14 ◯ 5 = 4

The following grid operates according to a specific pattern. Can you fill in the blank section?

10

Answer see page 130

06 You are faced with two doors, either of which might be wired to kill you as soon as you open it. Each door bears a sign. One of the signs is true, and one is false.

Which door should you open?

Sign A: This door is safe, but door B is deadly.

Sign B: One door is safe, and the other is deadly.

Answer see page 130

07 These triangles follow a specific logic. What should replace the question mark?

Answer see page 130

08

The following numbers obey a certain logic. What number should replace the question mark?

A	B	C	D	E
3	7	1	3	7
0	1	1	9	1
7	5	3	5	?
8	3	8	3	3
4	1	0	6	1

Answer see page 130

Answer see page 130

09

Three archers were practising their skills. After each had fired five shots, they paused to compare scores. Examining all three targets, each person made three statements, one of which was incorrect. Who scored what?

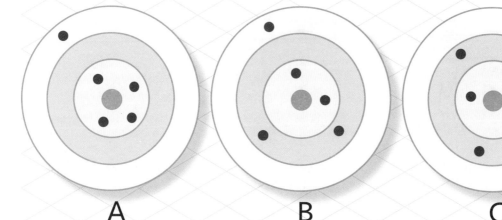

A

B

C

A: I scored 40 less than B. I scored 200. I scored 20 more than C.
B: C scored 260. I did not score lowest. There were 20 points between C and A.
C: A scored 220. I scored less than A. B scored 60 more than A.

Answer see page 130

10

A is to B as C is to V, W, X, Y or Z?

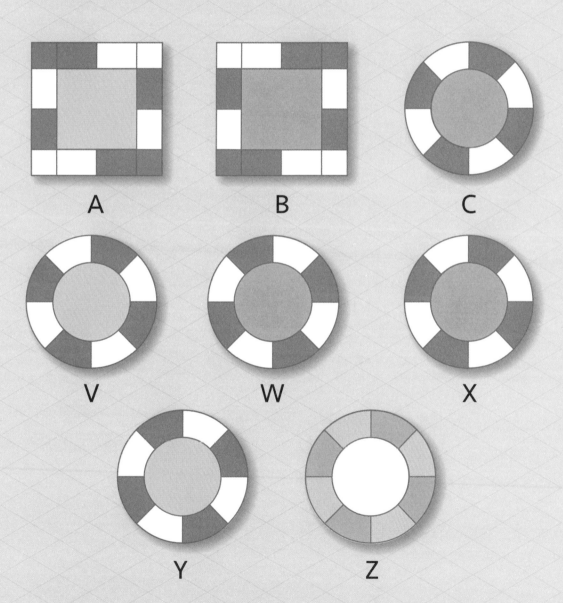

A   B   C

V   W   X

Y   Z

13

11

The following tiles have been taken
from a five by five square of numbers.
When they have been reassembled
accurately, the square will show the
same five numbers reading both
across and down.

Can you rebuild it?

Answer see page 130

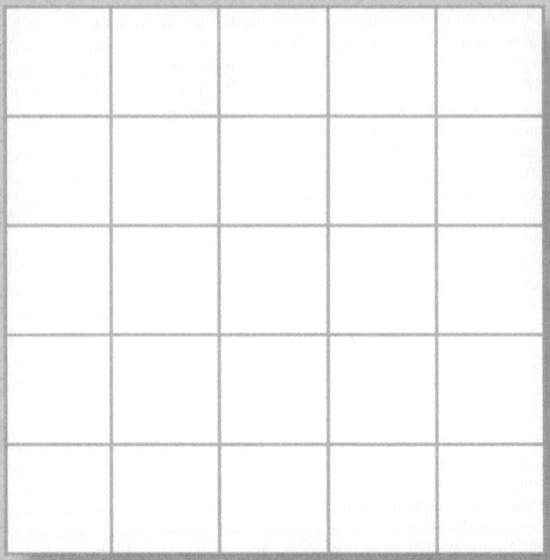

14

4	9	4

5	7

5	7

2	8	5

3
0
2

4
9
4

0
2
8

6
3

2
3

3
5

12

Can you draw three circles within the box so that each one completely encloses exactly one triangle, one square, and one pentagon? No two circles may enclose exactly the same three elements.

Answer see page 130

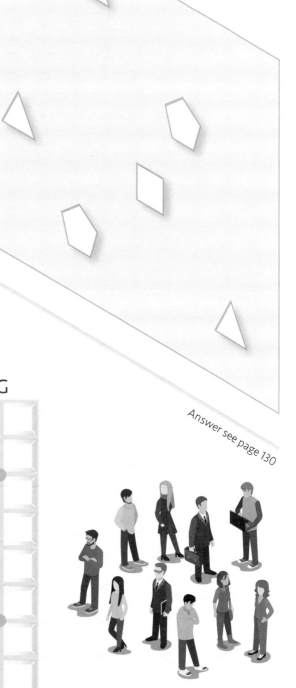

13

Ten people are in different locations are the city centre, and want to meet up. Which street corner should they pick to minimise their total combined journey?

Answer see page 130

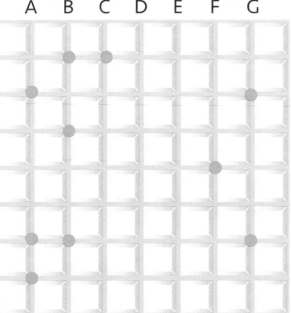

14

Ten people are sitting in two rows, facing each other, men on one side, and women on the other. From the information given below, can you say which desk Pip is at?

Pip is next to the woman opposite Richard. Adam is next to Tom. Alice is three desks away from Emily. Graham is opposite the woman next to Anita. Either John or Richard are at desk 8. The woman sitting next to the woman opposite desk 10 is Alice. Anita is opposite John. Tom is three desks from John. Adam is opposite Emily. Either Alice or Cassandra are at desk 3 and Desk 1 is opposite Desk 10.

Answer see page 130

15

The following five items are all famous US states. Can you decrypt them?

DMZUWVB

SMVBCKSG

WZMOWV

VMJZIASI

WSTIPWUI

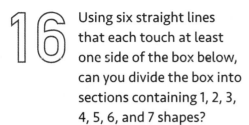

Using six straight lines that each touch at least one side of the box below, can you divide the box into sections containing 1, 2, 3, 4, 5, 6, and 7 shapes?

Answer see page 131

Can you tell what number comes next in this sequence?

Answer see page 130

2 3 5 7 11 13 ?

18 Two people are playing chess. Under the rules, a win is worth 2 points, a draw is worth one point, and a loss is worth 0. The pair start at 0 points, and after three rounds, A has four points, as does B. How is this possible?

Answer see page 131

Answer see page 131

19 These triangles follow a certain specific logic. What number should replace the question mark?

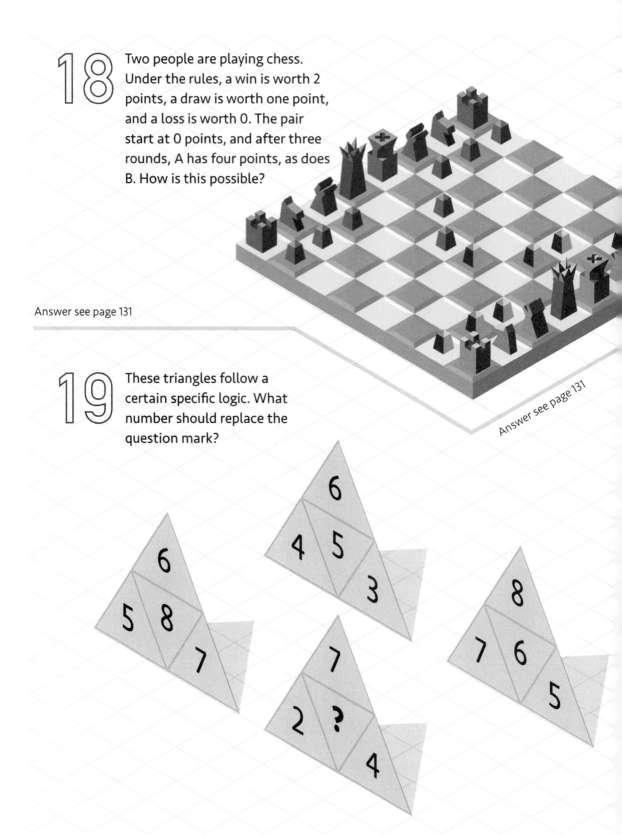

6
4 5
3

6
5 8
7

7
2 ?
4

8
7 6
5

20 Can you divide this square into four identical shapes, each one containing just one of each of the five symbols?

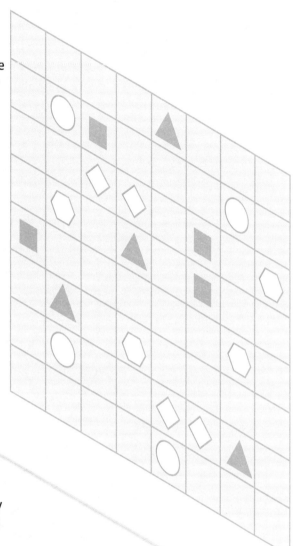

Answer see page 131

21 The following numbers obey a certain logic. What should replace the question mark?

Answer see page 131

4   9   21   45   81

6   14   32   62   ?

22 Can you place the segments below the triangular grid over the grid itself in such a way as to ensure that every node is covered by an identical symbol? Not all connecting lines will be covered.

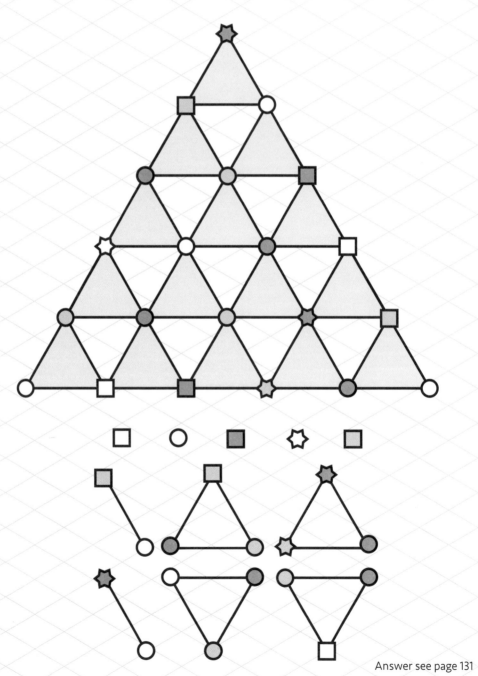

Answer see page 131

23

Can you fill in the numbers provided to correctly complete the grid?

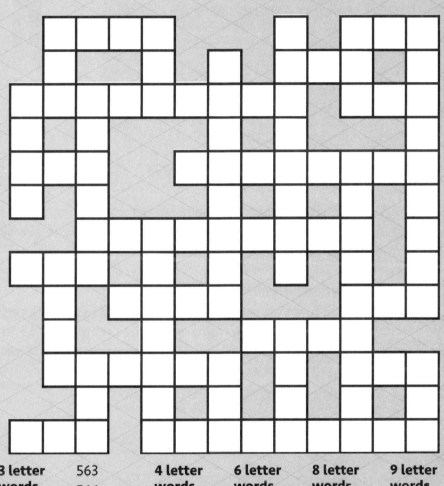

21

3 letter words	563	**4 letter words**	**6 letter words**	**8 letter words**	**9 letter words**
	566				
230	631	1870	342655	35464363	303952649
251	662	3822	821465	85156270	569429503
261	699	6748		96936352	643654970
366	713	6841	**7 letter words**		693039529
452	719	7908			936135966
475	843	8145	9780436		

Answer see page 131

24 You are faced with three men, A, B, and C, who know each other. Each of the three either always lies, or always tells the truth. Each makes one statement to you.

Which, if any, are definitely telling the truth?

You are unable to hear A's statement.
B: "A said that he is a liar."
C: "B is lying to you."

Answer see page 131

Answer see page 131

25 Signs – symbols in a specific position – which appear in the outer circles are transferred to the inner circle as follows: If it appears once, it is definitely transferred. If it appears twice, it is transferred if no other symbol will be transferred from that position. If it appears three times, it will be transferred if there is no sign appearing once in that position. If it appears four times, it is not transferred. In instances where signs with the same count are competeing, then from high to low, priority runs top left – top right – bottom left – bottom right. What does the inner circle look like?

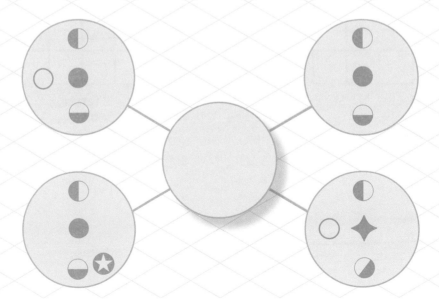

26 These circles function according to a certain logic. What number should replace the question mark?

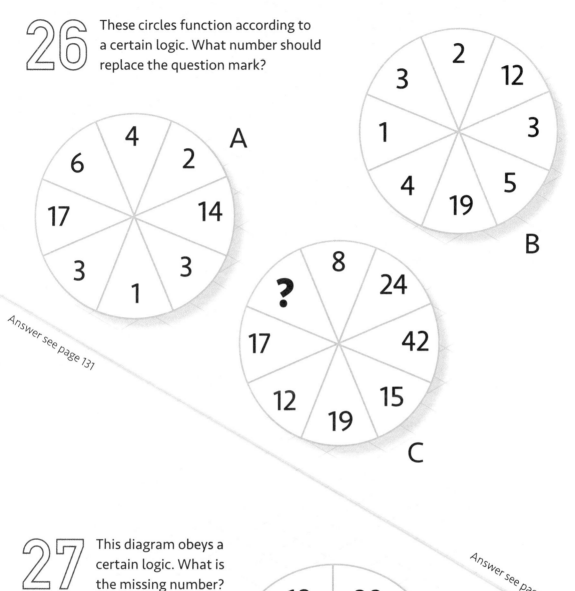

A

B

C

Answer see page 131

27 This diagram obeys a certain logic. What is the missing number?

Answer see page 131

28

In this long division calculation, each digit has been consistently replaced with a symbol chosen at random. Can you discover the original calculation?

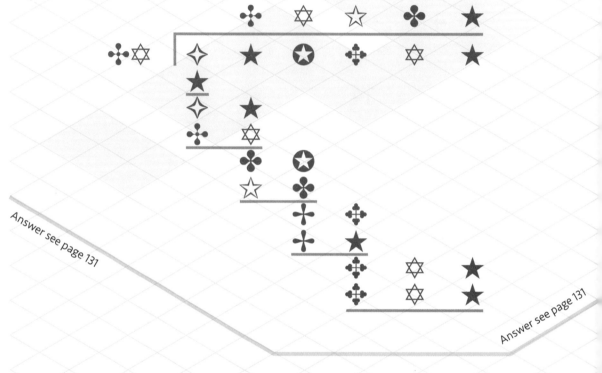

Answer see page 131

Answer see page 131

29

You come up with a theory, and ask three entirely separate scientists to evaluate how likely it is that you are correct. Each one works independently of the others, and there is no communication between them. After some time, you receive their reports. The first one says that the likelihood that you are correct is 80%. The second one also says that the likelihood that you are correct is 80%. Finally, the third one says that same as the other two – that the likelihood that you are correct is 80%.

What is the actual probability that your theory is correct?

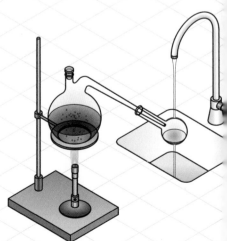

30

Which group of shapes, A–D, most closely corresponds with the conditions of the large group of shapes above?

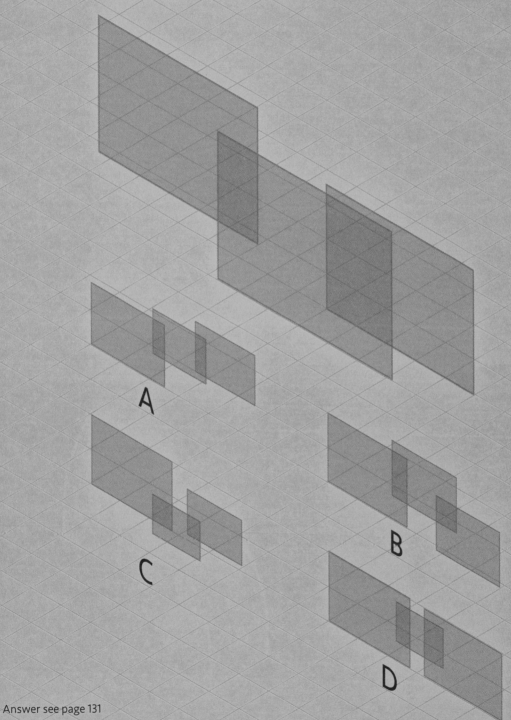

A

B

C

D

31 Following the logic of this diagram, what symbols should the triangle at the top contain?

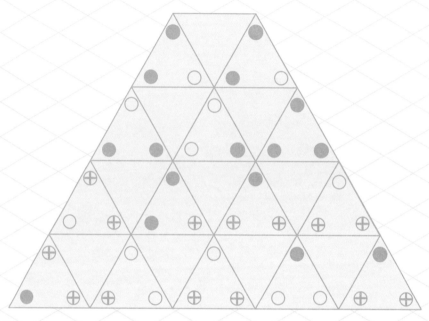

Answer see page 131

Answer see page 131

32 Two sealed bags, A and B, each contain either a bead or a pearl with equal probability. Someone then puts a pearl into bag B, shakes it, and randomly pulls out a pearl. You are then offered your choice of bag to open. Which is more likely to hold a pearl, if either?

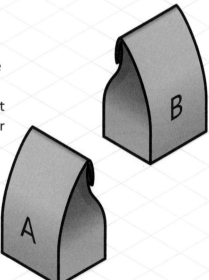

33

The letters and numbers in this square obey a certain logic. What number should replace the question mark?

Answer see page 132

34

Imagine a very large piece of very thin paper, its thickness one tenth of a millimetre. Cut it in half, and place the two halves on top of each other. Then cut the two halves, and restack to make four pieces. Continue in this fashion until you have cut a total of fifty times, assuming one cut is always enough to halve the stack, and that you are likewise tall enough to combine the two resulting piles back into one stack.

Approximately how tall is your stack after fifty cuts?

Answer see page 132

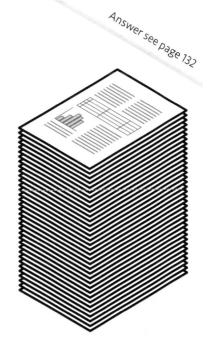

35 The following list of numbers represents cities whose letters have been encoded into the numbers needed to reproduce them on a typical phone numberpad. Can you decode them?

772 483

227 235 662

452 746 9

274 722 63

826 268 837

382 24

Answer see page 132

36 The word TROTTING is located exactly once in the grid below, but could be horizontally, vertically or diagonally forwards or backwards. Can you locate it?

T O T T R N G T T G R G T T T
T T T I I I G O I T T T T O T
T N G G I T G N T N R G G O T
N O T G O O N O I T G O R G T
T T I O T N T T T T O T O T I
R R G T T G R O I G T T T R
T O T I N I O T T N I O R T G
T T O N T T N O G R R T R R G
G G T I I G T N G I G O N T G
R G O T T I O R N T T T O G
R N R O T R N T I T T O R G T
T I R N N T G T T G G N I G T
G R G O T G T O O O N T T T T
T T O N R T N R T N T R G O O
O T I T T T N I N T R N O T N

Answer see page 132

37

Can you uncover the logic of this grid of letters and replace the question mark with the right letter?

D	I	B
C	E	G
H	A	?

Answer see page 132

Answer see page 132

38

These 12-hour digital clocks follow a specific logic. Can you work out the time of the fifth clock?

2

10 44 19

1

11 57 23

4

04 38 59

3

08 18 11

5

?? ?? ??

39 Look at the diagram below. What is the largest version of the same shape that can be drawn within the box so that none of its edges touch any other edges, or stray outside the box?

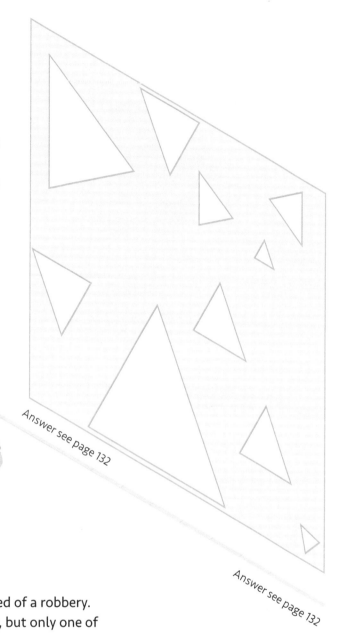

Answer see page 132

Answer see page 132

40 Three crooks are accused of a robbery. Each gives a statement, but only one of the statements is true.

Which one is telling the truth?

A: "B is lying"

B: "C is lying"

C: "A and B are both lying".

41 Figure #1 is to figure #2 as figure #3 is to which figure?

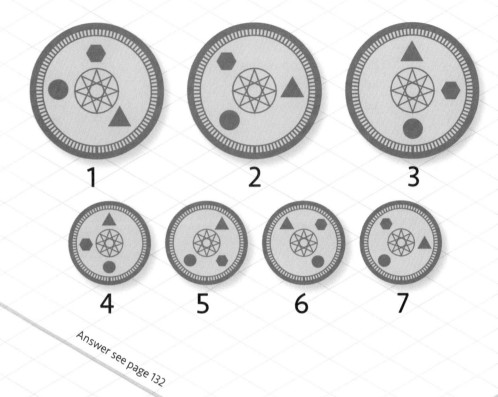

1   2   3

4   5   6   7

Answer see page 132

42 This set of diagrams follows a certain logic. What should replace the question mark?

Answer see page 132

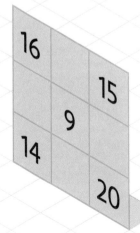

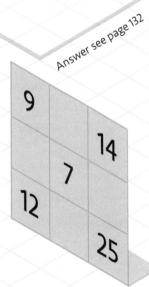

43 To which of the lower shapes, A-E, could a single ball be added so that both balls matched the conditions of the balls in the upper shape?

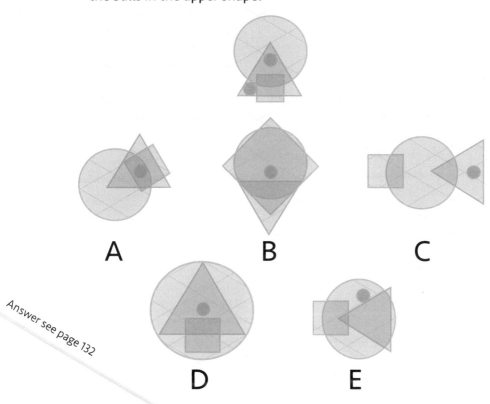

A

B

C

Answer see page 132

D

E

Answer see page 132

44 In a chess club of 60 people, 32 are female, 45 are adult, and 42 wear either glasses or contact lenses. What is the least possible number (not including zero) of people who fit all three categories?

45 Five people meet at a conference, and get talking. What is the favourite food of the person who was born in Oregon?

The person from Vermont loved cherries, and was neither Margaret nor Otis. The person who said duck was their favourite food was an engineer, and was not named Bobbie, who was born in Ohio. The botanist was not named Hersh or Angie. The person who loved lamb was a researcher. The person who was born in Louisiana did not love chocolate. Angie, who was born in Arizona, was not an engineer. Margaret was a doctor, and was not born in Oregon. One of the group was a farmer, and another had bread as their favourite food.

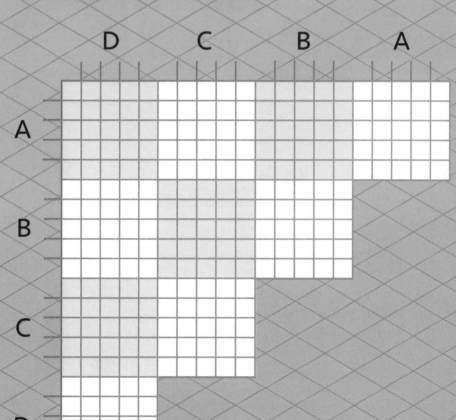

Answer see page 132

The diagram below operates according to a specific logic. What should the missing **square** look like?

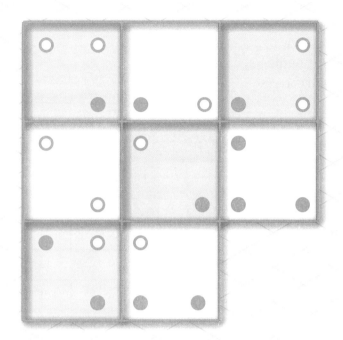

Answer see page 132

This set of diagrams follows a certain logic. What should replace the question mark?

Answer see page 132

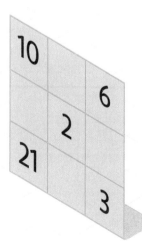

Answer see page 133

48

In the grid below, letters have been consistently replaced with the same random numbers. Can you complete the grid correctly?

36

	3		22		7				26		22		8	
15	21	2	24	20	2	14	12		21	9	21	24	25	21
	24		5		24		25		11		24		14	
15	2	17	18		12	25	10	2	11	21	24	2	6	25
	8				25		13		25		13		13	
7	4	25	25	9	19		11	4	14	13	7	2	17	6
		17		25		25				12		21		
	26	2	1	21	12	13		5	17	7	25	24	24	
	25		2			14		25		25				
25	12	25	17	11	21	11	25		6	5	14	25	24	19
	2		12		3		10		11				25	
3	13	24	24	13	23	5	2	21	24		11	6	21	14
	3		2		5		10		2		5		10	
20	14	5	17	25	2		25	17	17	13	20	24	25	6
	25		16		11			16			25		6	

1	2	3	4	5	6	7 W	8	9	10	11	12	13
14	15	16	17	18	19	20	21	22	23 Q	24 L	25	26

49

The following playwrights have had the vowels and spaces removed from their names. Can you untangle them?

STPHNPLKFF   GRGBRNRDSHW
SCRWLD   NKLGGL
JHNNWLFGNGVNGTH   RSTPHNS
FDRCGRCLRC   CHRSTPHRMRLW
LLLNHLLMN   SRHKN

Answer see page 133

50

One of the squares in the 3x3 grid is incorrect. Which one?

Answer see page 133

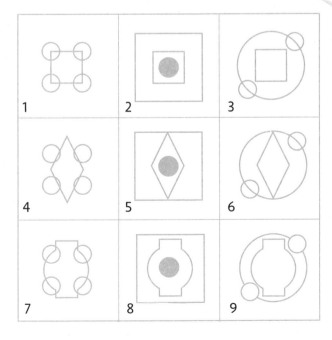

51 Can you rearrange the digits in this equation to make it correct, without adding any mathematical operators?

4 2 6 = 1

Answer see page 133

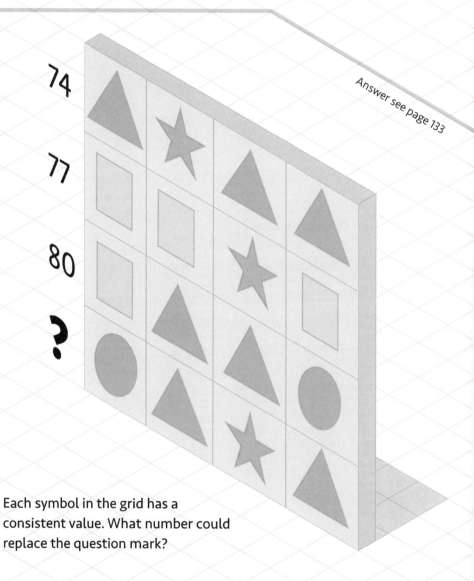

74
77
80
?

Answer see page 133

38

52 Each symbol in the grid has a consistent value. What number could replace the question mark?

53 Each square on this grid shows you the move you must make to arrive at the next square in the sequence, Left, Right, Up, and/or Down. So 3R would be three squares right, and 4UL would be 4 squares diagonally up and left. Your goal is to end up on the finish square, F, having visited every square exactly once. Can you find the starting square?

3R	1D	1L	2D	2L
3D	3R	2L	3D	2L
2R	1UR	F	3L	1L
3U	3R	2L	3L	3L
1R	1U	1UR	3U	
	1U	1R	2L	

Answer see page 133

39

54 These clocks obey a specific sequence. What time should the missing hour hand on the fourth clock be pointing towards?

Answer see page 133

3

1

2

?

55

Which of these shapes is the odd one out?

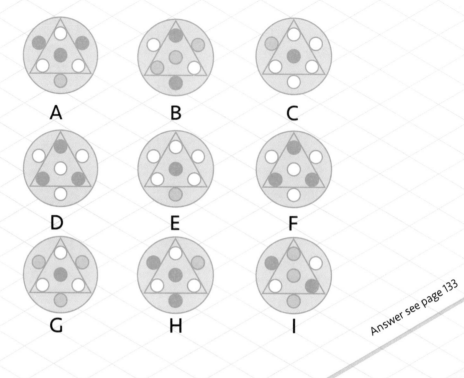

A

B

C

D

E

F

G

H

I

Answer see page 133

40

Answer see page 133

56

The following numbers obey a certain logic. What should replace the question mark?

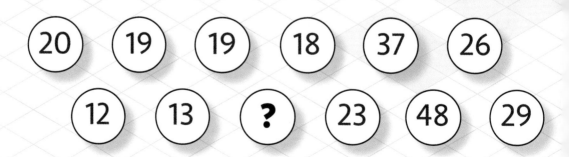

20 19 19 18 37 26

12 13 ? 23 48 29

57 Starting at any corner, follow the paths until you have five numbers, including the one where you started. Do not backtrack. Add the five together. What is the highest number you can obtain?

5 8

8 9 5

7

2

3 9

6

6

4 6

Answer see page 133

58 The following design works according to a certain logic. What number should replace the question mark?

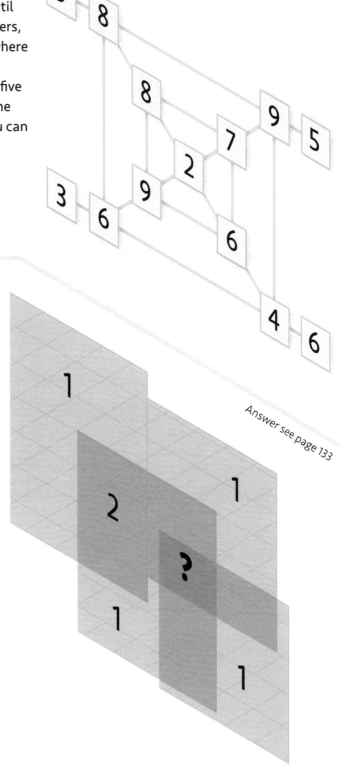

Answer see page 133

41

Answer see page 133

59 Four of these five pieces
fit together to make a
regular geometric shape.
Which one is left over?

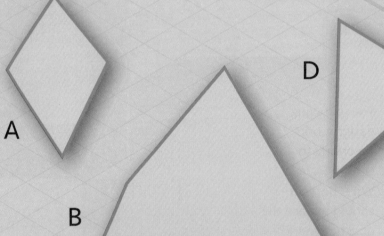

A

B

D

42

C

E

60

A race was run in four legs. Given the distances in kilometres of each leg, and the average speed in meters per second for that leg for the top five contestants, can you work out who won, and in what total time?

Runner	Leg Distance	A-B 4.5km	B-C 2.7km	C-D 3.3km	D-E 1.3km
V		4.4	3.3	4.8	5.1
W		4.7	2.9	4.4	5.0
X		4.1	3.7	4.3	5.1
Y		4.6	3.3	4.9	5.2
Z		4.5	3.4	4.6	5.1

Answer see page 133

61

Can you insert the mathematical operators + and – to make these equations valid?

Answer see page 133

12 ◯ 17 ◯ 9 ◯ 6 ◯ 14 = 12

26 ◯ 10 ◯ 4 ◯ 17 ◯ 11 = 14

15 ◯ 17 ◯ 9 ◯ 8 ◯ 13 = 16

62 Each of the circles below contains the name of a work of literature and its author. Can you unscramble them?

A

B

C

Answer see page 133

Answer see page 133

44

63 If Kelly likes rugby, Amarantha likes decathlon, and Jocasta likes sailing, which sport does Millie like?

A. Athletics

B. Snooker

C. Football

D. Tennis

E. Surfing

64

What weight will balance the beam?

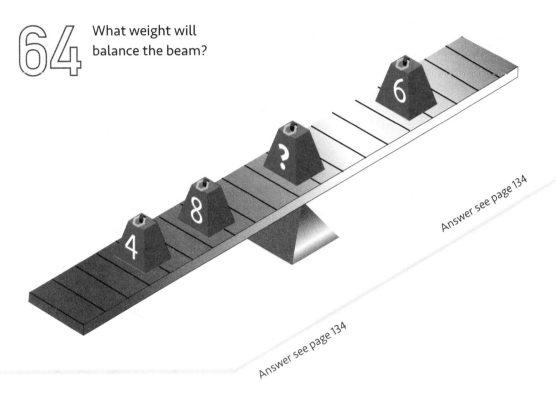

Answer see page 134

Answer see page 134

65

The matchstick diagram below shows five equal squares. Can you move 2 matchsticks to show just four equal squares?

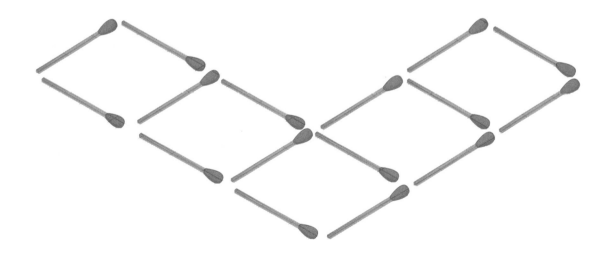

Examine the top three shapes.
Which of the five options A-E
continues the sequence ?

Answer see page 134

46

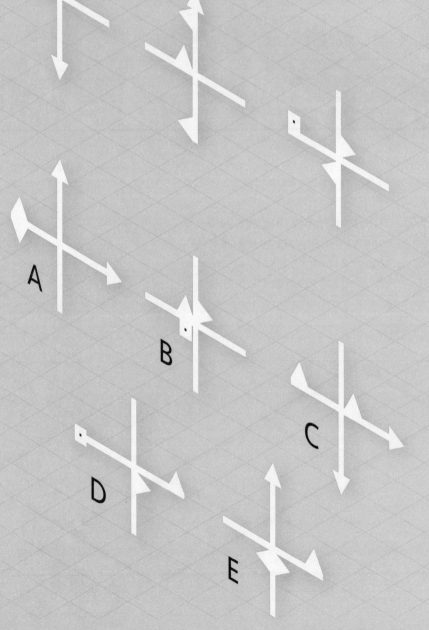

67 These rings obey a certain logic. What number should replace the question mark?

Answer see page 134

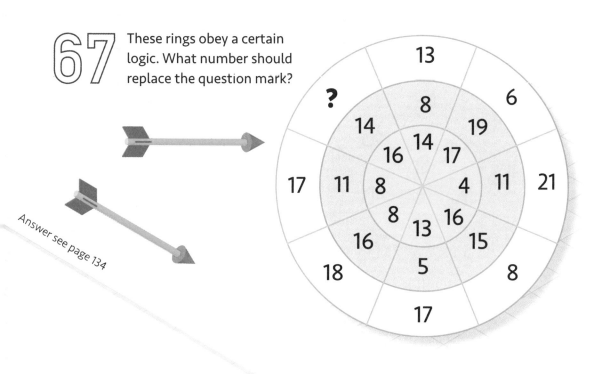

Answer see page 134

68 These triangles follow a certain specific logic. What number should replace the question mark?

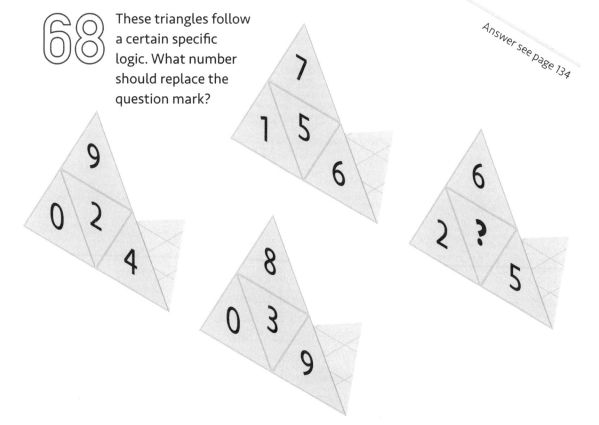

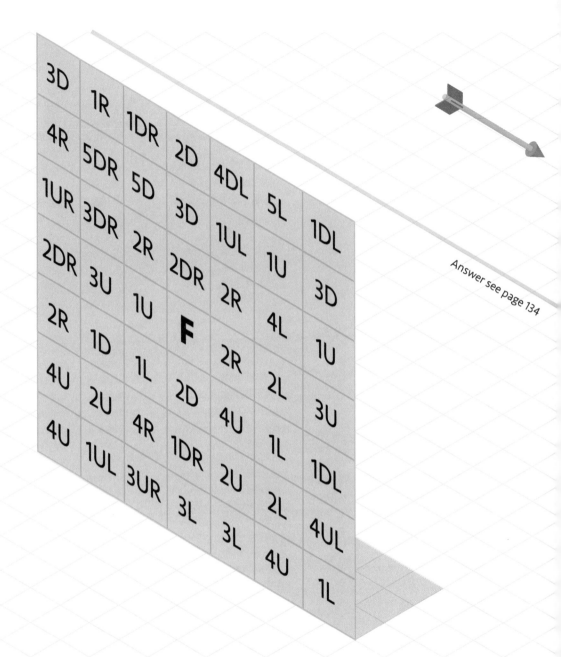

Each square on this grid shows you the move you must make to arrive at the next square in the sequence, Left, Right, Up, and/or Down. So 3R would be three squares right, and 4UL would be 4 squares diagonally up and left. Your goal is to end up on the finish square, F, having visited every square exactly once. Can you find the starting square?

Answer see page 134

70

These rings obey a certain logic. What letter should replace the question mark?

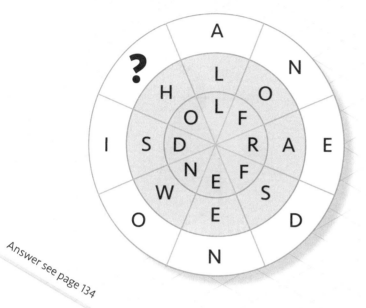

Answer see page 134

71

This set of diagrams follows a certain logic. What should replace the question mark?

Answer see page 134

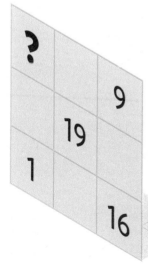

72 A bag holds four counters. One of them is white. Each of the others is either black or white at equal chance. You randomly draw out two counters, and discover they are both white. If you then randomly draw a third counter, what is the chance that it is white?

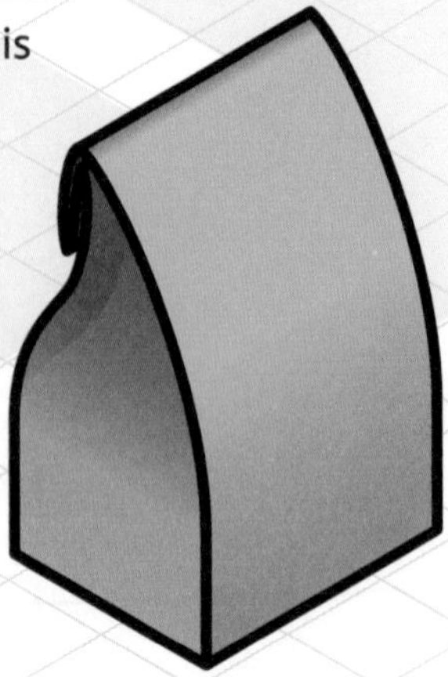

Answer see page 134

Answer see page 134

73 What weight will balance the beam?

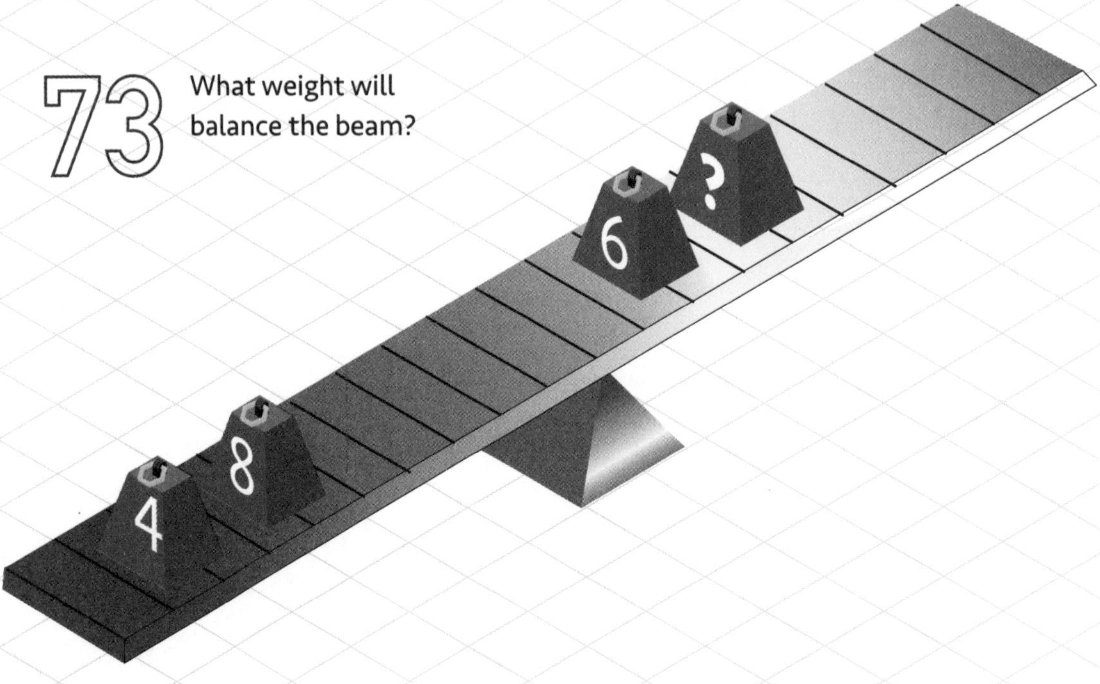

74 Can you divide up this board to correctly show the 28 dominoes listed below?

1	0	5	3	1	6	5	5
2	4	2	2	2	6	0	2
6	1	1	6	4	1	6	2
0	1	5	4	3	2	5	0
4	5	1	4	5	3	3	0
3	6	1	4	6	4	2	3
3	6	0	5	0	4	0	3

| 0 0 |
0 1	1 1
0 2	1 2	2 2
0 3	1 3	2 3	3 3
0 4	1 4	2 4	3 4	4 4
0 5	1 5	2 5	3 5	4 5	5 5
0 6	1 6	2 6	3 6	4 6	5 6	6 6

Answer see page 134

51

Answer see page 134

75 Anna's mother has four children that she is equally proud of. All of them are daughters, and have inherited her green eyes and red hair. The eldest was born in June, so has Rose as her birth flower, and is named Rose. The second eldest was born in July, so has Lily as her birth flower, and is named Lily. The second youngest was born in August, so has Poppy as her birth flower, and is named Poppy. The youngest was born in September, and has Aster as her birth flower. What is her name?

76 Following the logic of this diagram, what symbols should the triangle at the top contain?

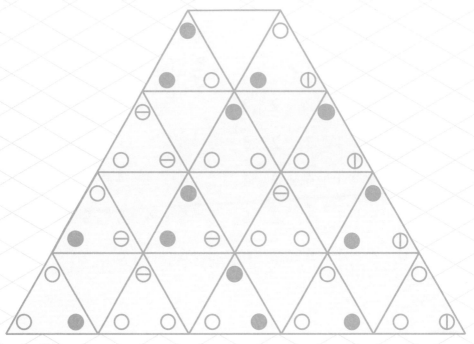

Answer see page 134

77 Can you uncover the logic of this grid of letters and replace the question mark with the right letter?

Answer see page 134

78

The following grid operates according to a specific pattern. Can you fill in the blank section?

79 The following numbers obey a certain logic. What should replace the question mark?

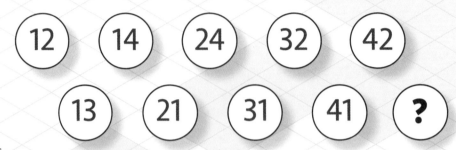

(12) (14) (24) (32) (42)

(13) (21) (31) (41) (?)

Answer see page 135

Answer see page 135

80 The following items are all famous drinks. Can you decrypt them?

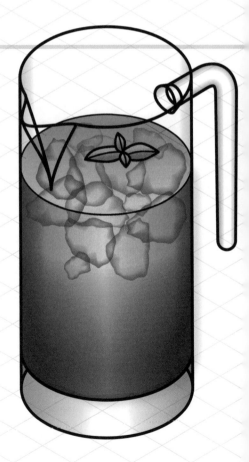

GUB PDUWLQL

PDQKDWWDQ

ROG-IDVKLRQHG

PDUJDULWD

GDLTXLUL

JLQ ILCC

PLQW MXOHS

81. If you were to walk a mile at 5mph, how quickly would you have to walk on the return journey to make your average speed there and back 10mph?

Answer see page 135

82. You have two different medicines that you take one pill of each day. The pills are indistinguishable. One morning, you realise that you have absent-mindedly taken out one pill from the first bottle, but two from the second. You have no idea which is which.

Is it possible to get the correct dose without throwing the three pills away?

Answer see page 135

83

The following tiles have been taken from a five by five square of numbers. When they have been reassembled accurately, the square will show the same five numbers reading both across and down.

Can you rebuild it?

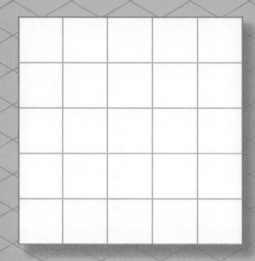

2 8 5

6 1 9

4
1
1

6
2
1

4
2

8
6

7

8 3   9 6   1 5   4 8

Answer see page 135

84

Which of these shapes
is the odd one out?

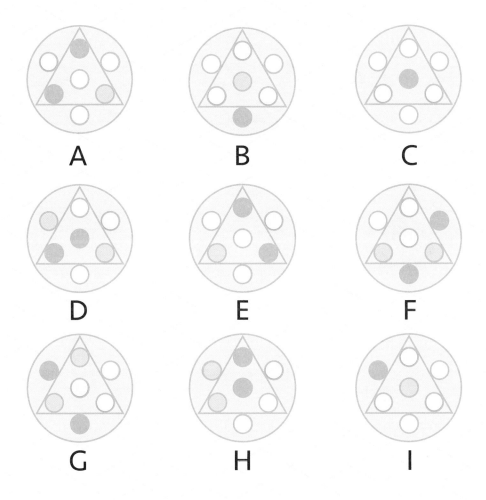

A

B

C

D

E

F

G

H

I

Answer see page 135

The following list of numbers represents items of furniture whose letters have been encoded into the numbers needed to reproduce them on a typical phone numberpad. Can you decode them?

268 683 786 7
752 973 6
268 462 227 727
273 336 92
743 326 273
825 526 9

Answer see page 135

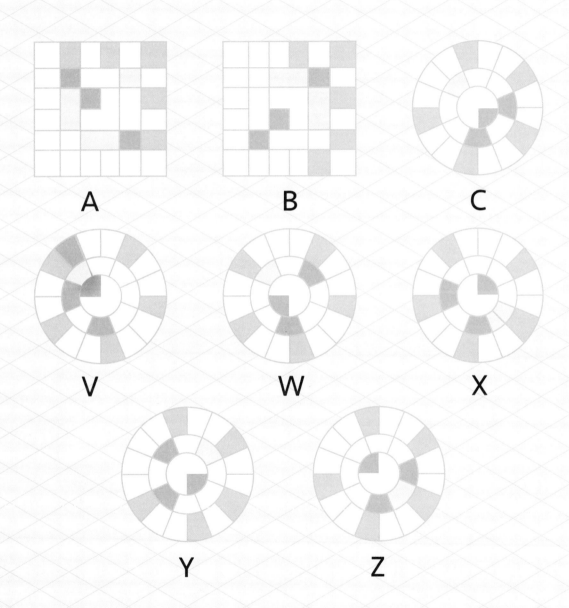

86

A is to B as C is to
V, W, X, Y or Z?

A

B

C

V

W

X

Y

Z

59

Answer see page 135

87

One of the squares in the 3x3 grid is incorrect. Which one?

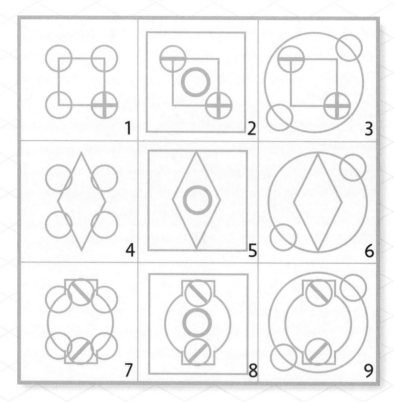

Answer see page 135

Answer see page 135

88

Can you tell what number comes next in this sequence?

10 6 13 1 13 10 10 1 19 ?

To which of the lower shapes, A-E, could a single ball be added so that both balls matched the conditions of the balls in the upper shape?

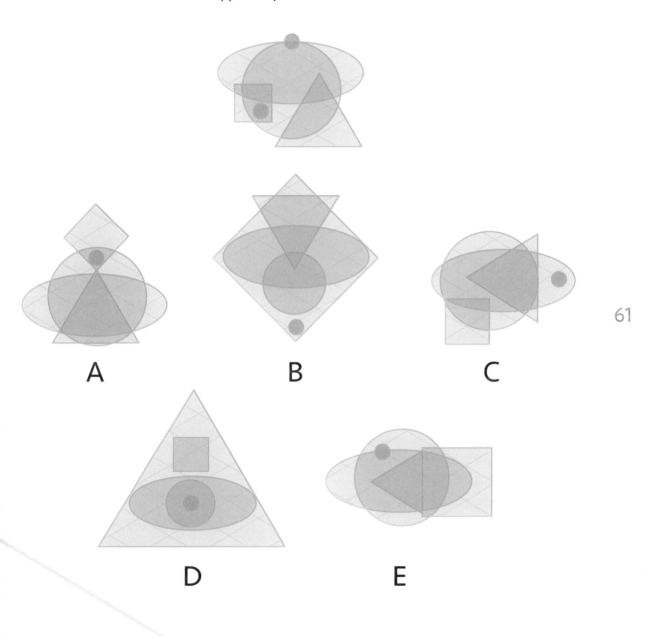

A

B

C

D

E

Answer see page 135

90 Can you divide this square into four identical shapes, each one containing just one of each of the five symbols?

Answer see page 135

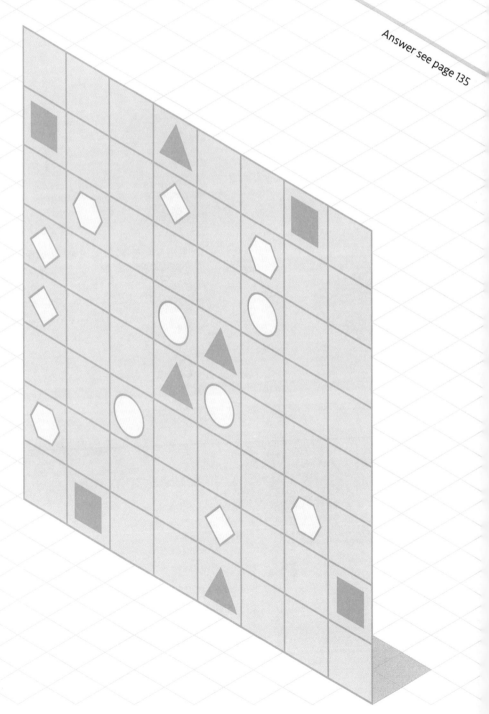

91 Each of the circles below contains the name of a work of literature and its author. Can you unscramble them?

Answer see page 135

Answer see page 135

92 In this long division calculation, each digit has been consistently replaced with a letter chosen at random. Can you discover the original calculation?

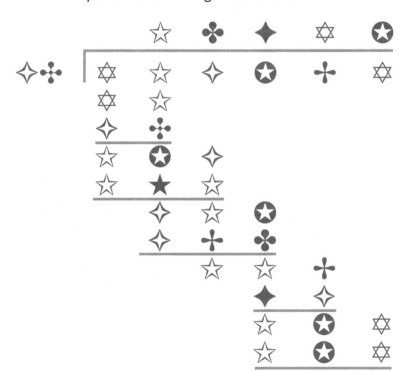

93 These columns observe a certain logic. What should the next column look like?

8

4 2

9 3 4

1 7 9

7 1 1

3 9 7

2 4 3 **?**

Answer see page 135

Answer see page 136

94 If Richmond likes Montreal but not Ottawa, Adrienne likes El Paso but not Naperville, Bartholomew likes Haboro but not Osaka, and Romaine likes Ioannina but not Naxos, which location does Mathilda dislike?

A. Fife
B. Glasgow
C. Leuchars
D. Dundrennan
E. Inverness

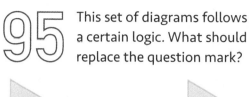

95 This set of diagrams follows a certain logic. What should replace the question mark?

13 7 71 9 18

29 5 37 12 9

18 11 ? 6 34

Answer see page 136

Answer see page 136

96 The following design works according to a certain logic. What number should replace the question mark?

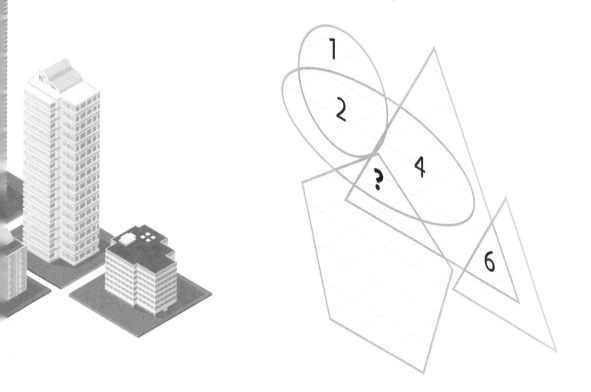

1
2
? 4
6

97

Five keen gardeners meet at a flower show, and compare their preferences. Which of the five had brought cheese sandwiches?

Hayden had brought ham sandwiches – but was not the person who was there to look at geraniums, who preferred red flowers. The person with chicken sandwiches preferred blue flowers, and was not there to look at pansies or a camellias. One person preferred pink flowers. Magdalena did not bring egg sandwiches. Thad did not bring egg sandwiches either, and wasn't there to look at geraniums. The person who'd brought tuna sandwiches was there to look at azaleas, and did not prefer white flowers. Liza was there to investigate delphiniums. Matt, finally, preferred purple flowers, and was not there to look at azaleas.

Which of the five had brought cheese sandwiches?

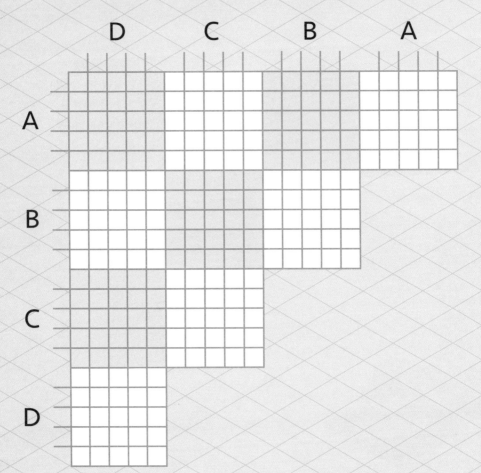

Answer see page 136

Each square on this grid shows you the move you must make to arrive at the next square in the sequence, Left, Right, Up, and/or Down. So 3R would be three squares right, and 4UL would be 4 squares diagonally up and left. Your goal is to end up on the finish square, F, having visited every square exactly once. Can you find the starting square?

2D	2R	4R	2R	4L	2D	3D
5R	2DR	1U	2L	4L	2D	3D
3R	2U	1D	3D	2L	1R	3D
2D	1L	2R	F	3U	4L	3D
2R	4R	3U	3U	1D	2L	3D
2R	1U	1D	2L	4U	1D	2L
2U	4U	1L	3L	4U	2L	2L

Answer see page 136

99 Using six straight lines that each touch at least one side of the box below, can you divide the box into sections containing 1, 2, 3, 4, 5, 6, and 7 shapes?

Answer see page 136

100 These triangles follow a specific logic. What should replace the question mark?

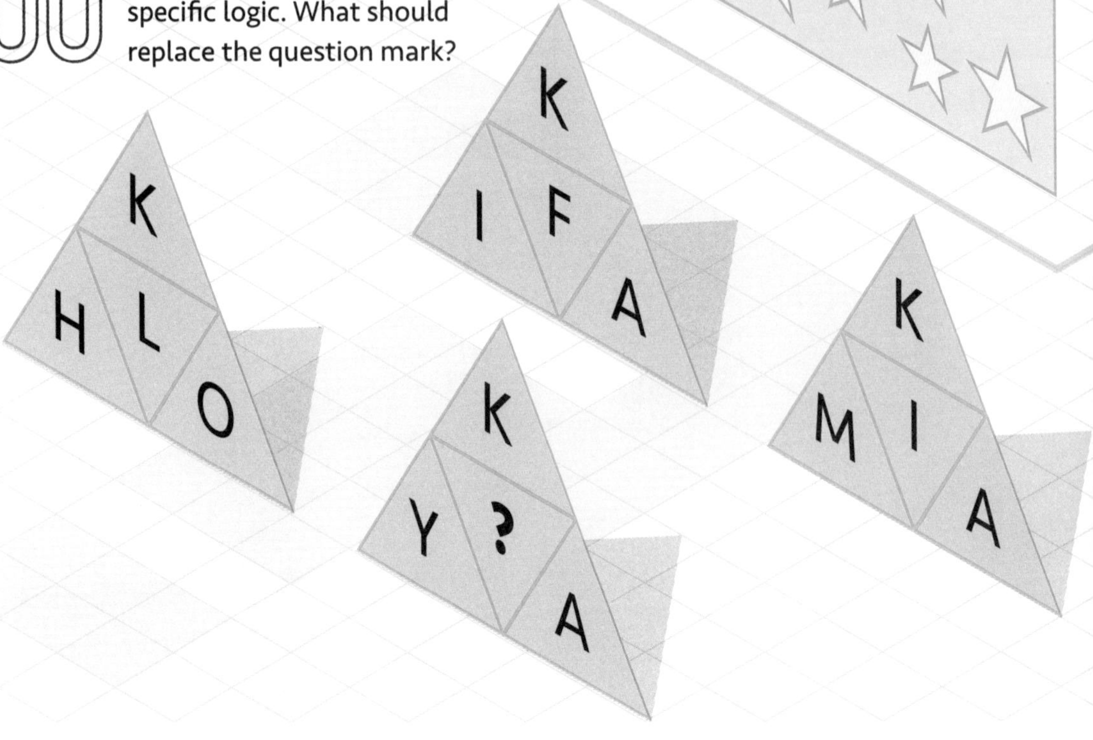

K
H L O

K
I F
A

K
Y ? A

K
M I A

101

These clocks obey a specific sequence. What should the time on the fourth clock be?

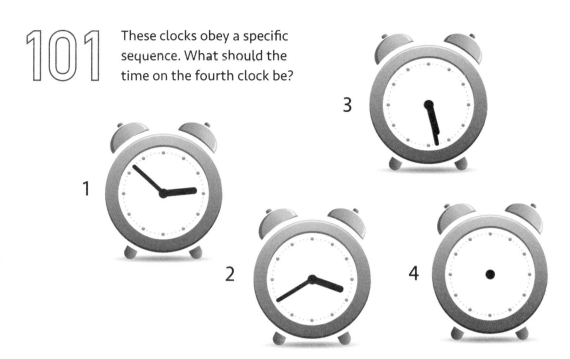

Answer see page 136

Answer see page 136

102

The letters and numbers in this square obey a certain logic. What number should replace the question mark?

103

These columns observe a certain logic. What should the next column look like?

4		
7		
3	5	1
9	1	4
6	1	1
4	9	0
1	9	1	?

Answer see page 136

70

Answer see page 136

104

Five crooks are accused of a robbery. Each gives a statement, but two of the statements are false. This is enough to give a decisive answer. Who is guilty?

A: It was B.

B: A is lying.

C: D is innocent.

D: E is innocent.

E: D is telling the truth.

105

A race was run in four legs. Given the distances in kilometres of each leg, and the average speed in meters per second for that leg for the top five contestants, can you work out who won, and in what total time?

Runner	Leg: Distance:	A-B 5.8km	B-C 4.6km	C-D 7.3km	D-E 0.9km
V		4.8	4.3	3.4	5.2
W		4.6	4.2	3.7	5.1
X		4.7	4.4	3.5	5.0
Y		4.9	4.25	3.1	5.4
Z		4.7	4.6	3.3	5.2

Answer see page 136

Answer see page 136

106

The diagram below operates according to a specific logic. What should the missing square look like?

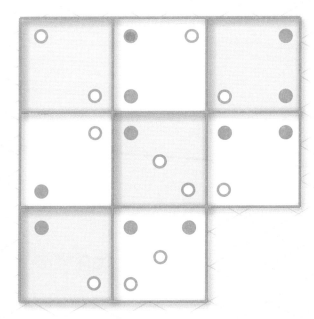

Each symbol in the grid has a consistent value. What number should replace the question mark?

72

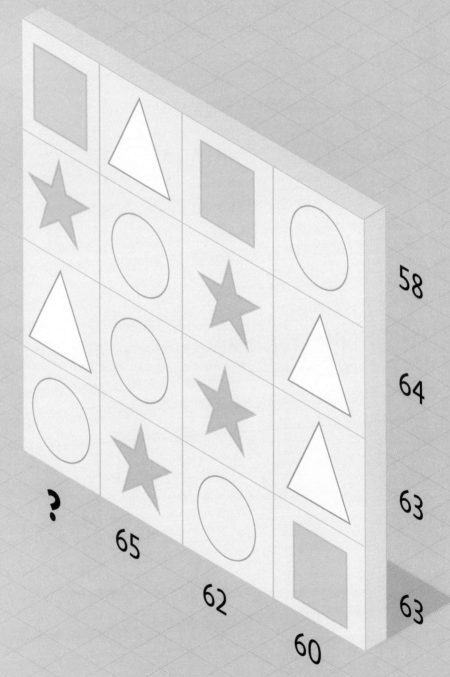

58

64

63

63

?

65

62

60

Answer see page 136

108

Can you place the segments below the triangular grid over the grid itself in such a way as to ensure that every node is covered by an identical symbol? Not all connecting lines will be covered.

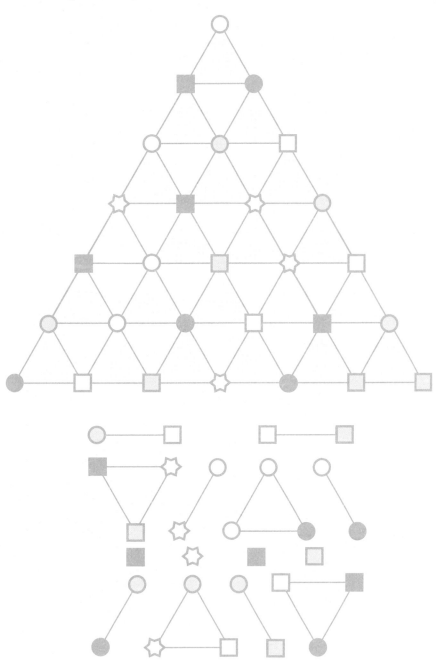

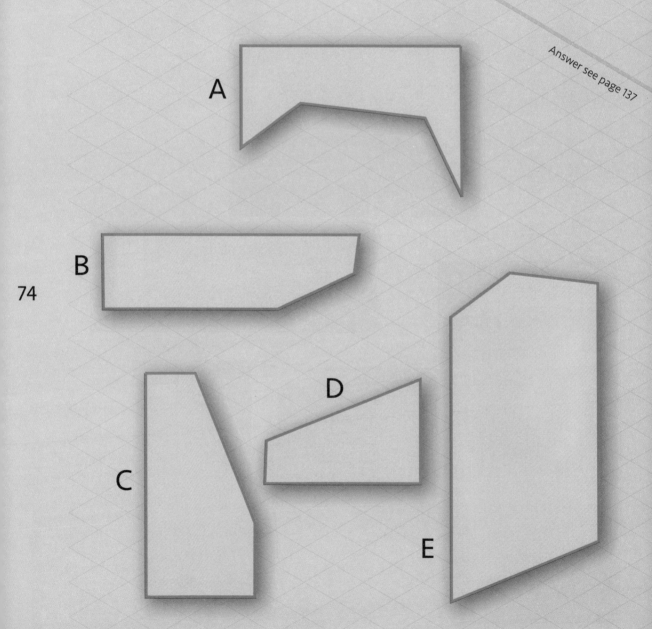

109 Four of these five pieces fit together to make a regular geometric shape. Which one is left over?

Answer see page 137

A

B

C

D

E

110 You are faced with two doors, either of which might be wired to kill you as soon as you open it. Each door bears a sign. The sign on door A is true if its door is safe, whilst the sign on door B is false if its door is safe. However, the signs have been removed from the doors, and you don't know which fits which.

Which door should you open?

Sign 1: This door is deadly.

Sign 2: Both doors are deadly.

Answer see page 137

Answer see page 137

111 This diagram obeys a certain logic. What is the missing number?

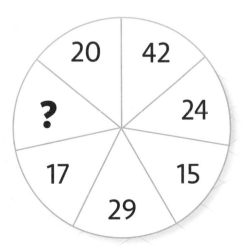

Can you fill in the numbers provided to correctly complete the grid?

Answer see page 137

76

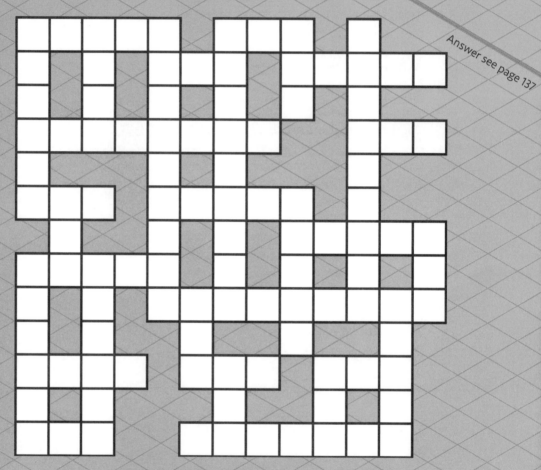

3 letter words

142	639
178	673
232	678
253	749
293	834
393	942
477	

4 letter words

3089
9112

5 letter words

10985
11624
18291
37255
51200
56071
73985

6 letter words

187127
277892
364382

7 letter words

7347385

8 letter words

11217966

9 letter words

215628072
326602260
524755252
937660985

113

Can you match the fragments to reassemble the names of several Hollywood celebrities?

NI	EY	BE	TON	JEN
LAW	BA	PET	KIN	DEN
HAL	ZEL	SON	HER	CY
CO	STOR	CAT	FER	RO
SHI	DEN	HEN	RRY	MIL
WA	EUVE	ER	INE	CHA
MARE	SA	RUS	AT	REN
CE	WAN	LE	RON	NG

Answer see page 137

Answer see page 137

114

You are faced with three women, A, B, and C, who know each other. One of the three always lies, one always tells the truth, and one either tells the truth or lies randomly. Each makes one statement to you.

Which is the one who always tells the truth?

A: B always tells the truth.

B: A is not the liar.

C: If you asked me, I'd say that B is random.

115 Examine the top three shapes.
Which of the five options A-E
continues the sequence ?

Answer see page 137

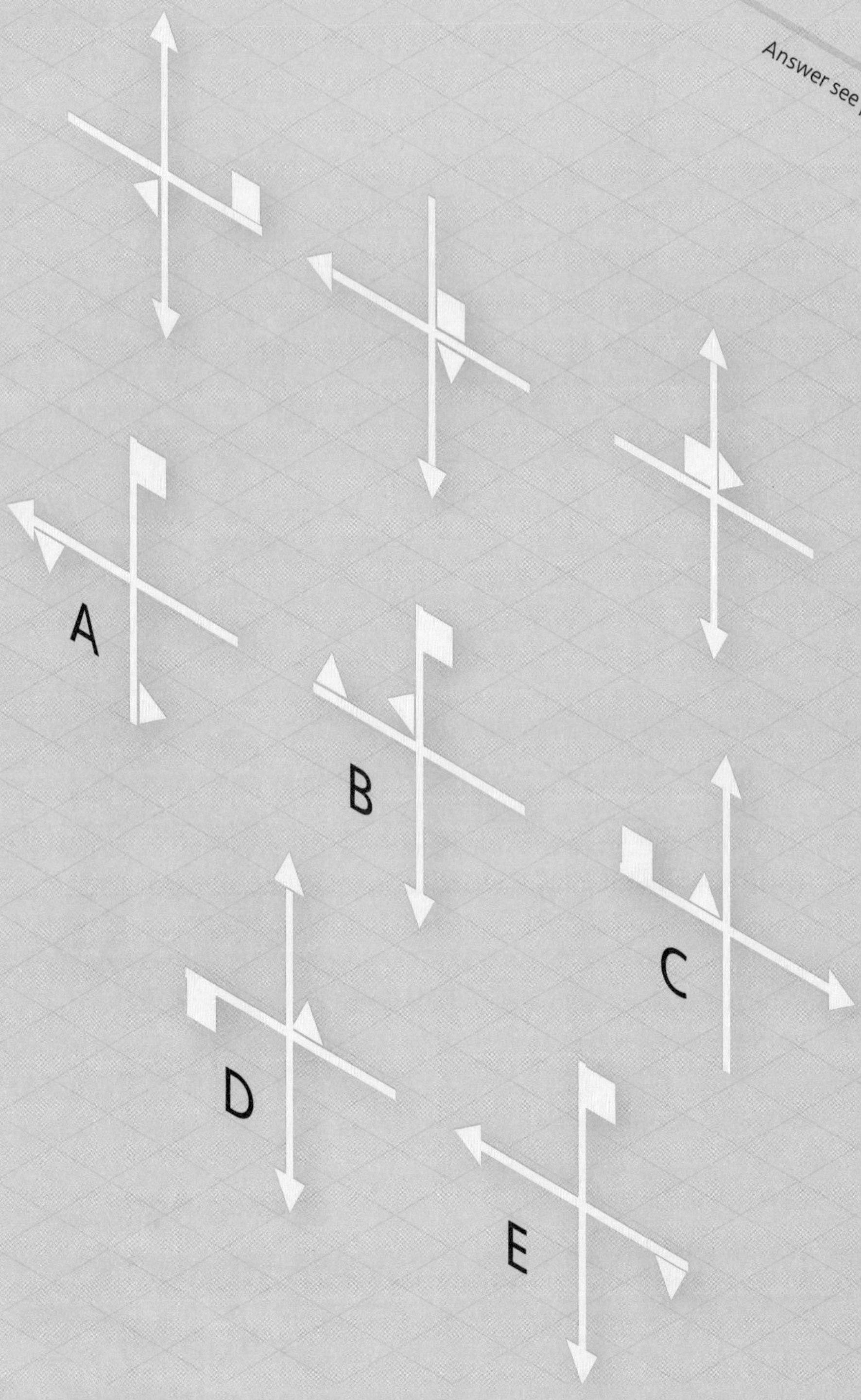

A

B

C

D

E

116

How many of the following statements are true?

- At least one of these statements is false.
- At least two of these statements are false.
- At least three of these statements are false.
- At least four of these statements are false.
- At least five of these statements are false.
- At least six of these statements are false.
- At least seven of these statements are false.
- At least eight of these statements are false.
- At least nine of these statements are false.
- All ten of these statements are false.

Answer see page 137

117

Which group of shapes, A-D, most closely corresponds with the conditions of the large group of shapes above?

Answer see page 137

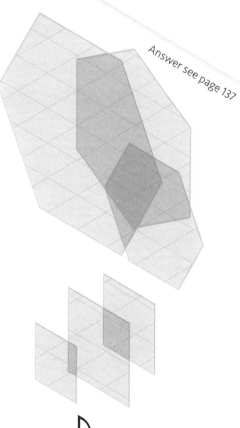

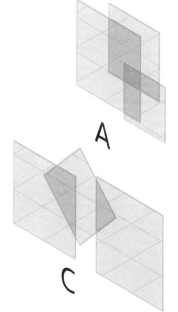

A

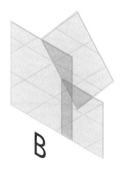

B

C

D

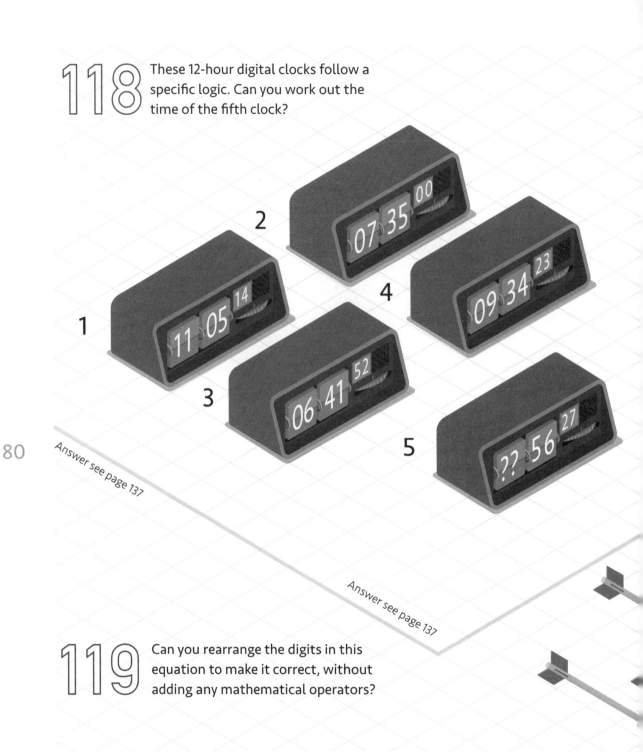

118

These 12-hour digital clocks follow a specific logic. Can you work out the time of the fifth clock?

2 07 35 00

1 11 05 14

4 09 34 23

3 06 41 52

5 ?? 56 27

Answer see page 137

Answer see page 137

119

Can you rearrange the digits in this equation to make it correct, without adding any mathematical operators?

4 4 = 9 3

120

Can you tell what number comes next in this sequence?

| 3 | 13 | 1113 | 3113 | 132113 |

Answer see page 137

Answer see page 137

121

Three archers were practising their skills on the same boss. After each had fired five shots, they paused to compare scores, and discovered that they had each scored 78 points. During evaluation, they noted that A had scored thirteen with the first two shots, whilst C had scored 8 with the final two. Who did not get a bulls-eye?

1
3
4
5
10
15
25
50

Answer see page 137

122

In the grid below, letters have been consistently replaced with the same random numbers. Can you complete the grid correctly?

82

	2	4	12	16	16	19	11	9	12	4	10	7	26	
18		7		4		26		13		7		15		19
19	18	8	25	7		12	26	19	18	12	2	19	17	26
14		25		7		26		2		11		22		2
7	20	22	7	9	13	7	4	7		2	25	2	17	4
10		7		13				20				20		17
18	19	22	13	7	12	4		19	26	3	21	7	2	22
7				7		17		7		26				15
2	17	2	12	20	20	24		22	11	17	4	19	12	7
12		12				12				9		26		11
15	17	8	17	14		20	19	18	7	20	19	6	13	2
13		20		7		18		12		7		4		19
17	5	7	4	8	17	12	4	10		10	19	12	1	17
4		12		7		22		12		6		2		26
	23	25	19	11	3	2	7	18	15	7	4	7	10	

1	2 T	3	4	5	6	7	8	9	10	11	12	13
14	15	16	17 O	18	19	20 L	21	22	23	24	25	26

123

Follow this set of simple instructions. What is the result?

1. Write down the number 7.
2. Subtract 3 from the last number you wrote down, and remember the result.
3. Write down the number you are remembering next to the last number you wrote down.
4. Add 2 to the last number you wrote down, and remember the result.
5. Write down the number you are remembering next to the last number you wrote down.
6. Add 2 to the last number you wrote down, and remember the result.
7. Have you written down at least nine digits? If no, go back to 2, else proceed.
8. Write down the number 1 next to the last number you wrote down.
9. Stop.

Answer see page 138

Answer see page 138

124

Examine the following sets of scales, which are in perfect balance. How many balls are needed to balance the final scale?

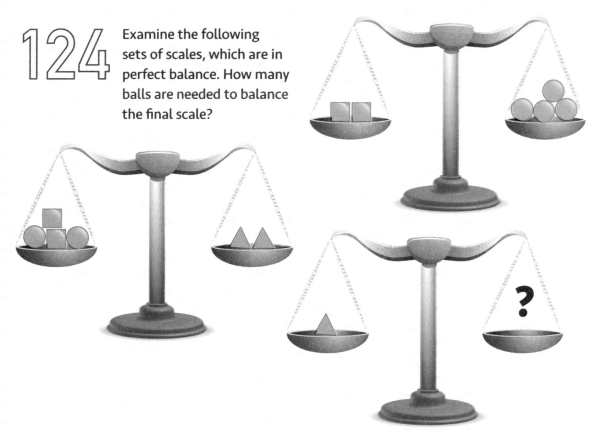

125

Examine the following sets of scales, which are in perfect balance. How many balls are needed to balance the final scale?

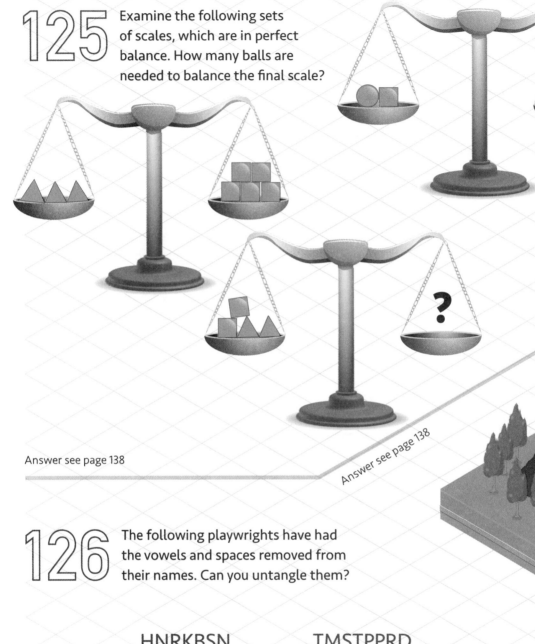

Answer see page 138

Answer see page 138

126

The following playwrights have had the vowels and spaces removed from their names. Can you untangle them?

HNRKBSN   TMSTPPRD

LXNDRSTRVSK   THRNTNWLDR

MKHLBLGKV   PRRCRNLL

HRLDPNTR   JHNSBRN

MGLDCRVNTS   JNRZDLRCN

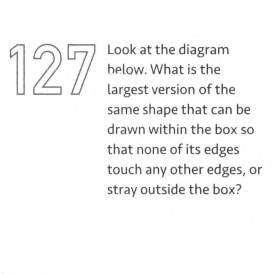

127 Look at the diagram below. What is the largest version of the same shape that can be drawn within the box so that none of its edges touch any other edges, or stray outside the box?

Answer see page 138

Answer see page 138

128 Amongst a group of thirty-eight mountaineers, twelve have successfully climbed Everest, seven have successfully climbed K2, two have successfully climbed the Dawn Wall, and all but six have successfully climbed Annapurna. What is the least possible number of people who have successfully climbed just one of the four?

129

The word THROAT is located exactly once in the grid below, but could be horizontally, vertically or diagonally forwards or backwards. Can you locate it?

Answer see page 138

```
H T T O T T R T T A T R A H R
O A A R H T O T R O A O R T R
T T H A T A T T H A H T H A T
O R R T R T A T R O H R T H O
T T O T T O A T O R T T H O T
H A A R T A O A R T R T O O R
T R T R O T T R T T H H R A O
T H T R H T R H O H T R O H O
T O R H R R R A T O H O O T O
R O H T T A O A H H T H O R T
R T T R A T O O R H O T T R H
R A T T T T O R O T T O T O
R T T T R H R O T T H A O T A
R T T A O A A H T A T A R T H
A H O A H T T T O A H T R R T
```

130

Fill in the underlined spaces below using only the digits 0-9, so that the following statement is truthful:

In the five lines below, there are

__ instance/s of the number 1;   __ instance/s of the number 2;   __ instance/s of the number 3;   __ instance/s of the number 4; and   __ instance/s of the number 5.

Answer see page 138

Answer see page 138

131

Signs – symbols in a specific position – which appear in the outer circles are transferred to the inner circle as follows: If it appears once, it is definitely transferred. If it appears twice, it is transferred if no other symbol will be transferred from that position. If it appears three times, it will be transferred if there is no sign appearing once in that position. If it appears four times, it is not transferred. In instances where signs with the same count are competeing, then from high to low, priority runs top left – top right – bottom left – bottom right. What does the inner circle look like?

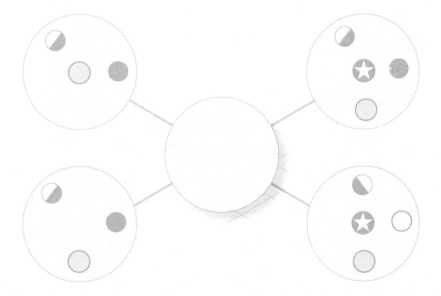

132

Can you draw three circles within the box so that each one completely encloses exactly one triangle, one square, and one pentagon? No two circles may enclose the same three elements.

Answer see page 138

133

The Roman numeral equation spelled out with matchsticks below is incorrect. Can you add just one matchstick to form a correct equation?

Answer see page 138

134 Ten people are sitting in two rows, facing each other, men on one side, and women on the other. From the information given below, can you say which desk Andy is at?

Either David or Richard are at desk 8. Either Debbie or Caroline are at desk 3. Either Amber or April are at desk 4. Sean is only sitting next to one person. Debbie is three desks away from Amber. Bernard is opposite the woman next to Lisa. Lisa is opposite David. Sean is next to Andy and opposite Amber. Andy is three desks from David, and desk 1 is opposite desk 10.

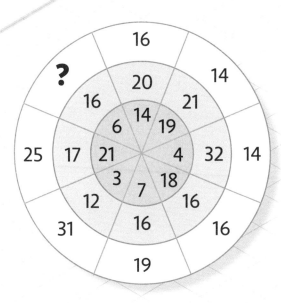

Answer see page 138

Answer see page 138

135 These rings obey a certain logic. What number should replace the question mark?

136

There are two bags. One, A, contains a single counter, either white or black at equal chance. The other, B, contains three counters, two black and one white. A white counter is added to A. A is then shaken, and a counter drawn randomly, which proves to be white. Your goal is to randomly draw a white counter from one of the two bags. Is it better to flip a coin to select a bag to draw from at random, or is it better to pour both A and B into a single third bag, C, and draw a counter from there?

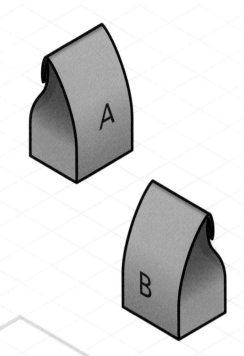

Answer see page 138

90

137

The following numbers obey a certain logic. What number should replace the question mark?

Answer see page 138

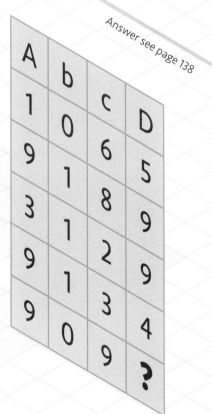

A	b	c	D
1	0	6	5
9	1	8	9
3	1	2	9
9	1	3	4
9	0	9	?

138

Starting in the centre rather than in a corner, follow the paths until you have five numbers, including the one where you started. Do not backtrack. Add the five together. What is the highest number you can obtain?

Answer see page 139

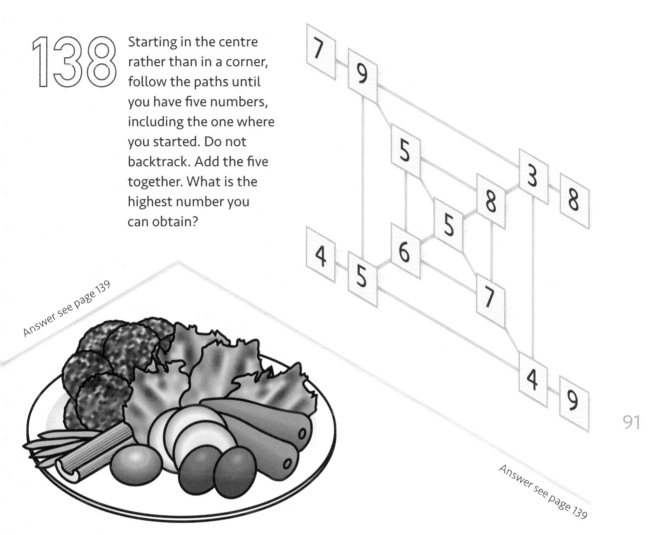

Answer see page 139

139

The following items are all foods. Can you decrypt them?

QPIITCQTGV RPZT

DPIBTPA

THRPAXKPSP

FJDGC

RDGCTS QTTU

YPBQPAPNP

GPIPIDJXAAT

YTGZN

140

Which group of shapes, A-D, most closely corresponds with the conditions of the large group of shapes above?

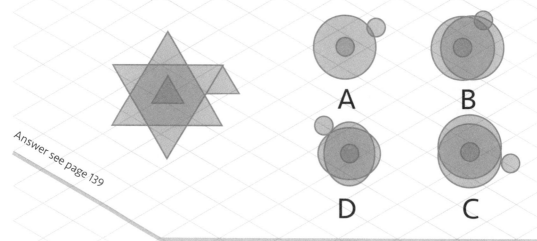

A

B

D

C

Answer see page 139

Answer see page 139

141

Can you place the segments below the triangular grid over the grid itself in such a way as to ensure that every node is covered by an identical symbol? Not all connecting lines will be covered.

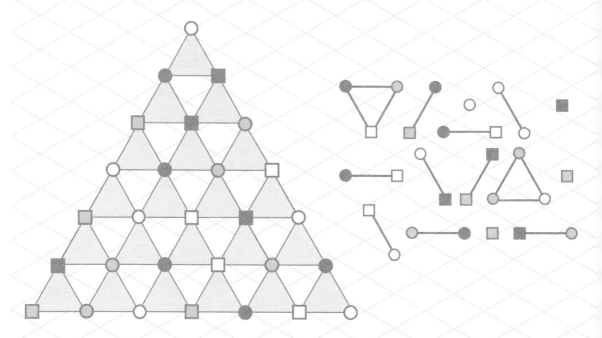

142

Figure #1 is to figure #2 as figure #3 is to which figure?

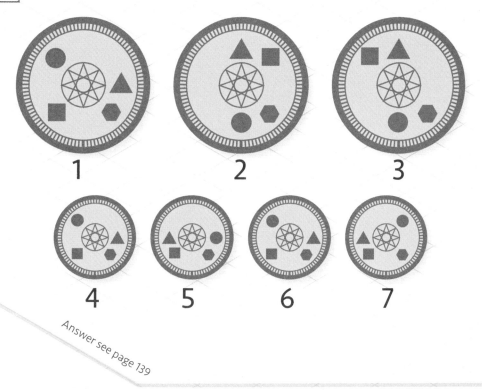

1   2   3

4   5   6   7

Answer see page 139

Answer see page 139

143

I find a piece of wood on the ground, one that I have never seen before. I pick it up, heft it thoughtfully, and then throw it. The piece of wood travels a reasonable distance before stopping completely. It then starts heading back towards me, arriving back finally to my hand again. It does not bounce or ricochet in any way, nor did I have anything tied to it. What happened?

144 Look at the diagram below. What is the largest version of the same shape that can be drawn within the box so that none of its edges touch any other edges, or stray outside the box?

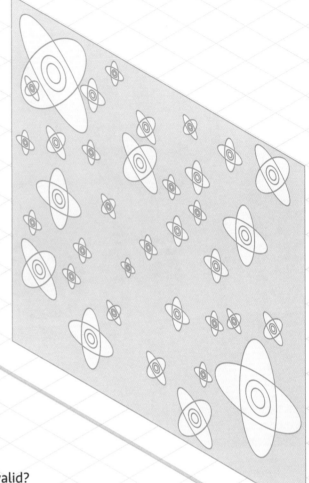

Answer see page 139

94

145 Can you insert the mathematical operators:
+ − * / ^ . √ ! ( )
to make these equations valid?

Answer see page 139

A   4 2 3 4 8 = 4

B   2 5 4 2 4 3 = 1 7

C   5 5 5 5 5 5 5 5 = 5 5

146

Using six straight lines that each touch at least one side of the box below, can you divide the box into sections containing 1, 2, 3, 4, 5, 6, and 7 shapes?

Answer see page 139

147

This diagram obeys a certain logic. What could be the the missing number?

Answer see page 139

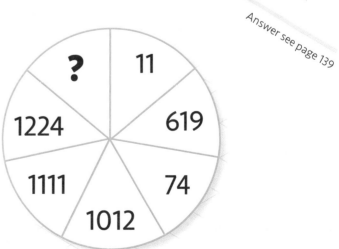

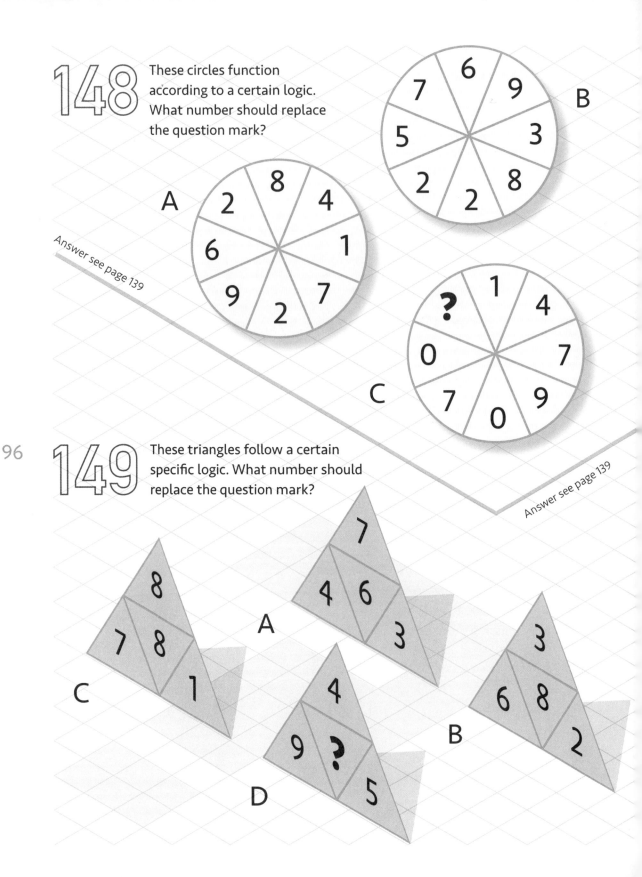

148 These circles function according to a certain logic. What number should replace the question mark?

A

B

C

Answer see page 139

96

149 These triangles follow a certain specific logic. What number should replace the question mark?

A

B

C

D

Answer see page 139

150

Can you fill in the numbers provided to correctly complete the grid?

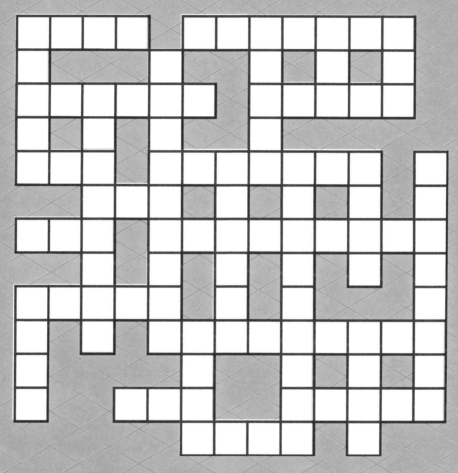

3 letter words	**4 letter words**	**5 letter words**	**6 letter words**	**7 letter words**	**8 letter words**	**9 letter words**
310	3410	12870	637251	5037593	36534897	148028558
417	4476	32570	854708	9581646	78783756	154331455
537	5536	34131				456941301
548	6414	36397				693352634
874	6848	98604				
963	9590					

Answer see page 139

151

Can you divide this square into four identical shapes, each one containing just one of each of the five symbols?

Answer see page 140

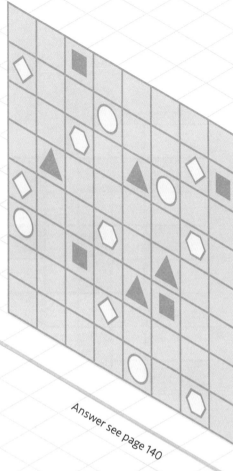

Answer see page 140

152

What weight will balance the beam?

153

Starting at any corner, follow the paths until you have five numbers, including the one where you started. Do not backtrack. Add the five together. What is the highest number you can obtain?

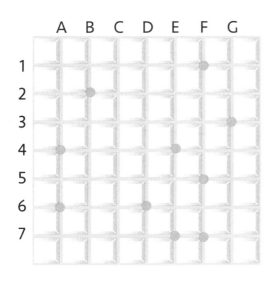

Answer see page 140

Answer see page 140

154

Ten people are in different locations in the city centre, and want to meet up. Which street corner should they pick to minimise their total combined journey?

155

A group of friends decided to spend a day practising some survival skills. They persuaded their most competent friend, Wolfgang, to put them through their paces in a number of situations. He declared himself the General for the day, tested them all, and after each hour, assigned them promotions or demotions according to the table below.

Answer see page 140

Wolfgang's scoring was as follows. Hour 0: Everyone starts at private. Hour 1: Lito promoted by one, Riley by twice Lito's promotion, Nomi by twice Riley's promotion, and Capheus by twice Nomi's promotion. Hour 2: Kala promoted to First Sergeant, Sun promoted to two above Kala, Will placed four below Sun. Hour 3: Sun and Capheus both promoted by 2, Will by 1. Kala demoted by 1. Hour 4: Riley demoted by 1. Kala busted down to private. Nomi made a Captain. Hour 5: Everyone who was promoted after the first hour is again promoted by 1. Hour 6: Sun promoted by 2, Will by 4, and Kala by 1. Hour 7: Capheus demoted by 4. Riley promoted by 3, Kala by 2, and Nomi by 1.

Who did best, and what rank are they?

1. General
2. Brigadier
3. Colonel
4. Lieutenant-Colonel
5. Major
6. Captain
7. First Lieutenant
8. Lieutenant
9. First Sergeant
10. Sergeant
11. Corporal
12. Private

Figure #1 is to figure #2 as figure #3 is to which figure?

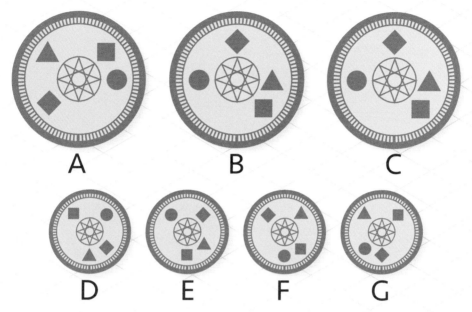

A   B   C

D   E   F   G

Answer see page 140

Answer see page 140

157

Three students are each taking four out of six subjects, so that each of the six subjects has two of the three students in it. From the information below, can you say which two study physics?

If Anna is studying mathematics, then she is also studying engineering. If she is studying engineering, then she is not studying programming. If she is studying programming, then she is not studying Japanese.

If Flora is studying programming, then she is also studying Japanese. If she is studying Japanese, then she is not studying mathematics. If she is studying mathematics then she is not studying micro-electronics.

If Susie is studying micro-electronics then she is not studying mathematics. If she is not studying mathematics, then she is studying Japanese. If she is studying Japanese, then she is not studying programming.

158 Can you draw three circles within the box so that each one completely encloses exactly one triangle, one square, and either one pentagon or one oval? No two circles may enclose the same three elements.

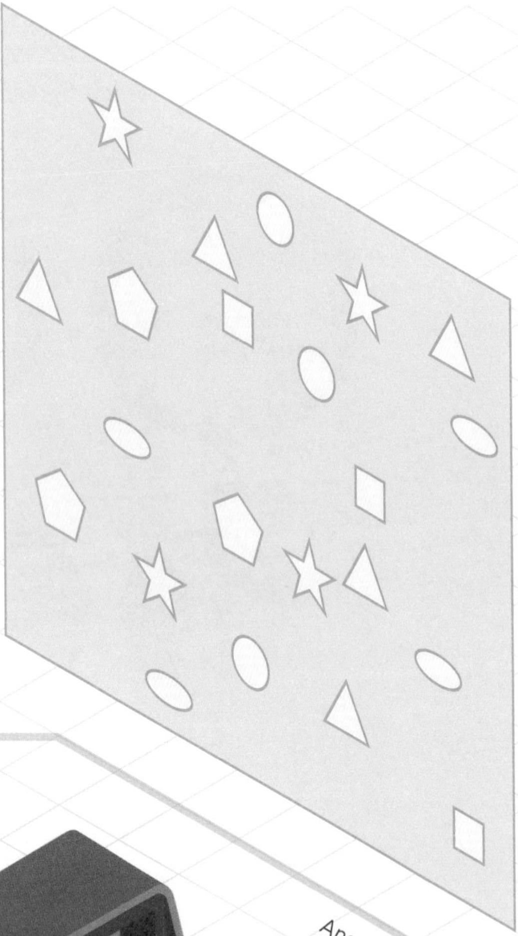

Answer see page 140

159 These 12-hour digital clocks follow a specific logic. Can you work out the time of the fifth clock?

Answer see page 140

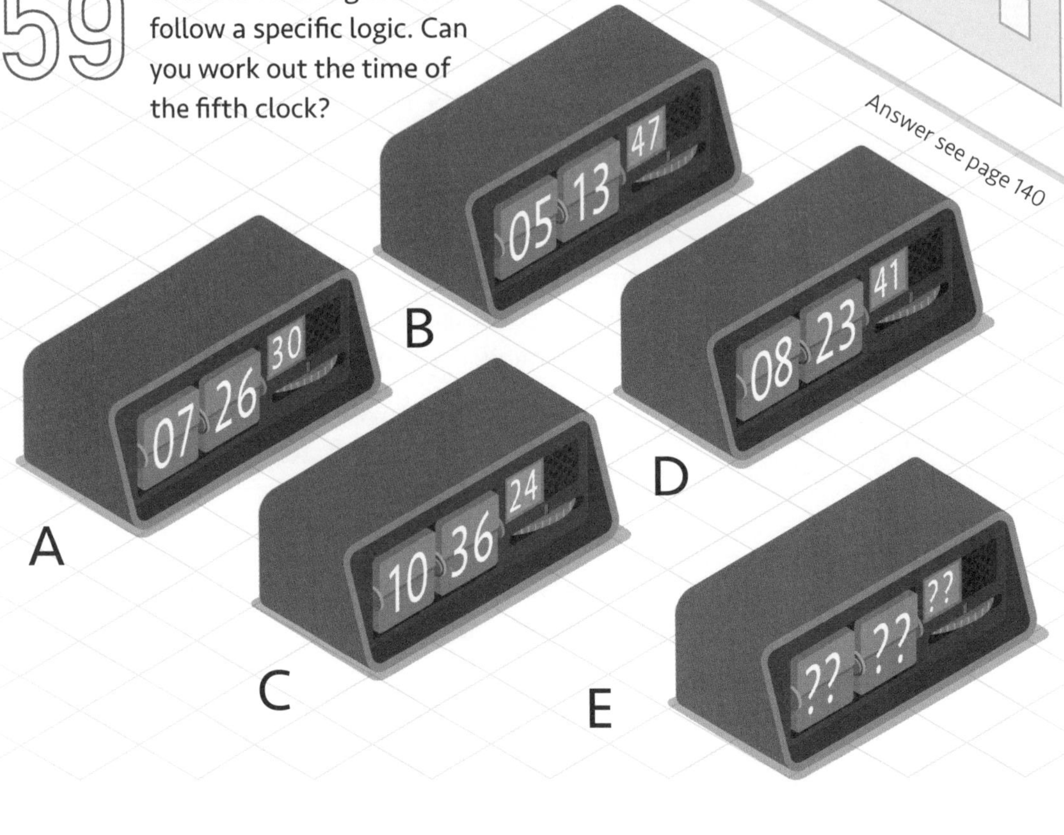

B 05 13 47

D 08 23 41

A 07 26 30

C 10 36 24

E ?? ?? ??

To which of the lower shapes, A-E, could a single ball be added so that both balls matched the conditions of the balls in the upper shape?

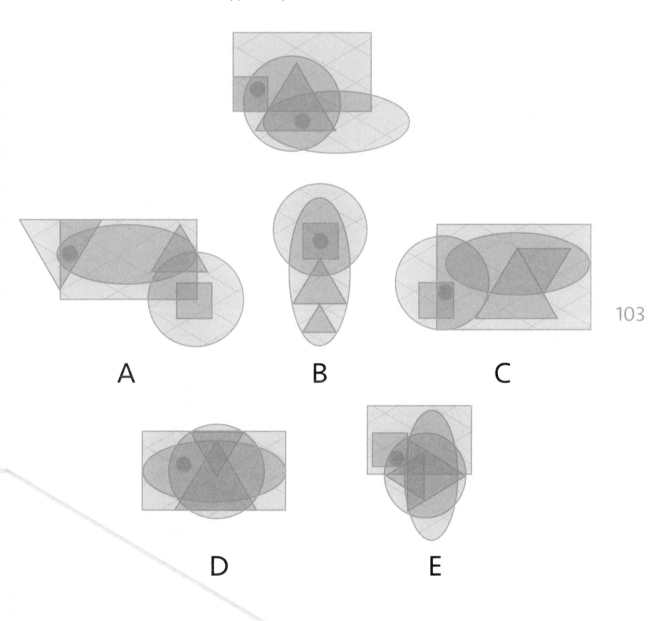

A

B

C

103

D

E

Answer see page 140

161 The following numbers obey a certain logic. What number should replace the question mark?

Answer see page 140

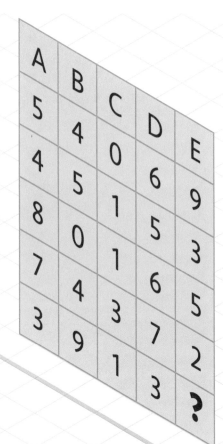

A	B	C	D	E
5	4	0		
4	5		6	
8		1		9
	0		5	
7		1		3
	4		6	
3		3		5
	9		7	
		1		2
			3	
				?

162 Amongst a group of 114 highly-dedicated bird watchers, 86 have seen an ivory-billed kingfisher, 77 have seen a kirtland's warbler, 92 have seen a whooping crane, 26 have seen a nene, and 57 have seen a piping plover. What is the least possible number of people who have seen just two of the five?

Answer see page 140

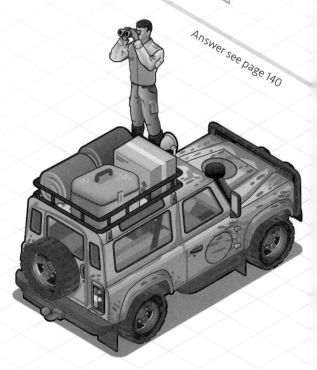

163

Each symbol in the grid has a consistent value. What number should replace the question mark?

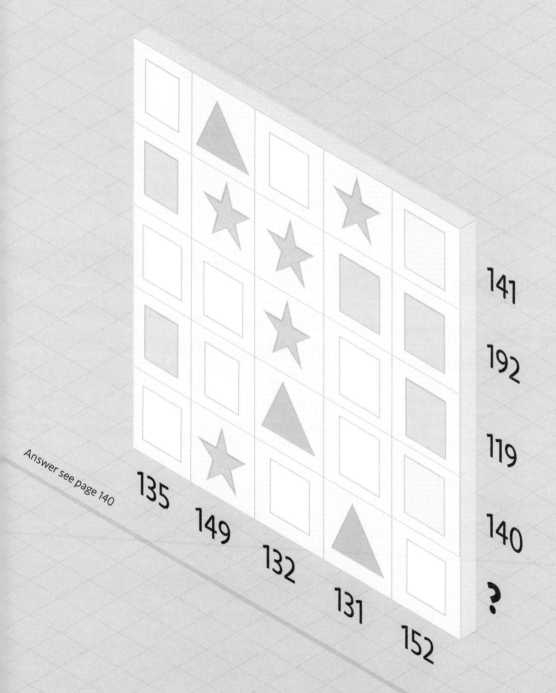

141

192

119

140

?

135

149

132

131

152

Answer see page 140

164

Which of these shapes is incorrect?

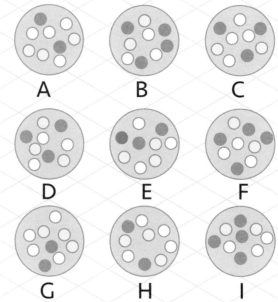

A

B

C

D

E

F

Answer see page 140

G

H

I

Answer see page 140

165

Following the logic of this diagram, what symbols should the triangle at the top contain?

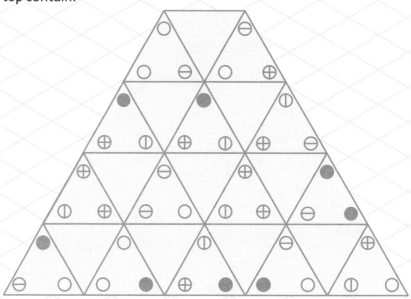

166 Following this set of simple instructions is supposed to turn any number of your choice into the same number. However, there is an error, and it doesn't work. What's wrong?

1. Choose any number and write it down.
2. Subtract 1 from the last number you wrote down and remember the result.
3. Write down the number you are remembering
4. Multiply the last number you wrote down by 3 and remember the result.
5. Write down the number you are remembering.
6. Add 12 to the last number you wrote down and remember the result.
7. Write down the number you are remembering.
8. Divide the last number you wrote down by 2 and remember the result.
9. Write down the number you are remembering.
10. Add 5 to the last number you wrote down and remember the result.
11. Write down the last number you are remembering.
12. Subtract the first number you wrote down from the last number you wrote down and remember the result.
13. Write down what you are remembering.
14. If the last number you wrote down was 8, say SUCCESS otherwise say FAILURE.
15. Stop.

Answer see page 141

Answer see page 141

167 These clocks obey a specific sequence. What time should the missing hour hand on the fourth clock be pointing towards?

3

1

2

4

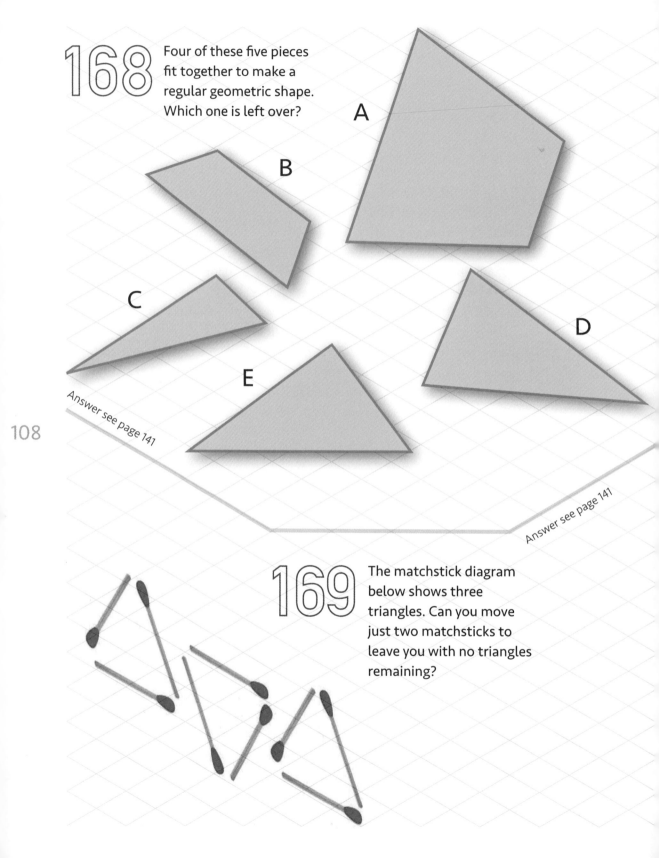

168 Four of these five pieces fit together to make a regular geometric shape. Which one is left over?

A

B

C

D

E

Answer see page 141

Answer see page 141

169 The matchstick diagram below shows three triangles. Can you move just two matchsticks to leave you with no triangles remaining?

170 You are faced with three people, A, B, and C, who know each other. They are standing in that order, where A is on the left as you look at them. One of the three always lies, one always tells the truth, and one either tells the truth or lies randomly. You are allowed to ask three yes or no questions, each one to be answered by a single person of your choosing. Which three questions, directed to which people, will uncover the truthful member of the three?

Answer see page 141

Answer see page 141

171 A highly competitive race was run in five legs. Given the distances in kilometres of each leg, and the average speed in meters per second for that leg for the top five contestants, can you work out who won, and in what total time?

	Leg:	A-B	B-C	C-D	D-E	E-F
Runner	Distance:	2.4km	2.6km	2.5km	2.7km	2.3km
V		4.65	4.52	4.32	3.81	5.23
W		4.67	4.51	4.35	3.79	5.22
X		4.71	4.49	4.31	3.80	5.24
Y		4.68	4.51	4.29	3.82	5.23
Z		4.72	4.52	4.30	3.79	5.21

172 Can you rearrange the digits in this equation to make it correct, without adding any mathematical operators?

$$6 \; 6 \; = \; 2 \; 3 \; 4$$

Answer see page 141

Answer see page 141

173 Examine the following sets of scales, which are in perfect balance. How many balls are needed to balance the final scale?

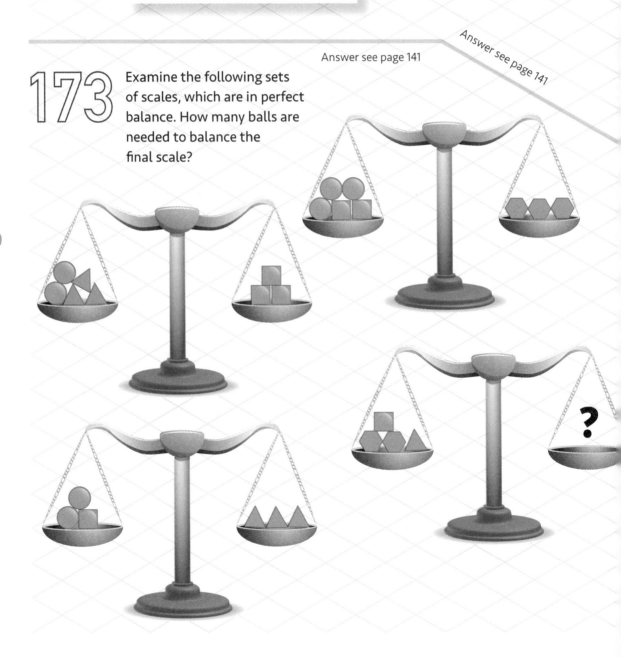

174

The following playwrights have had the vowels and spaces removed from their names. Can you untangle them?

JNCCT
LBRTCMS
SMNRZ
MRTNMCDNGH
SNCTHNGR
SHLGHDLN

GRGBCHNR
LFRHKRSMNRSN
PRRDMRVX
STPHNSNDHM
TRCLTTS
KLDS

175

Ten people are going to different locations in the city centre, and want to meet up afterwards. Which street corner should the tenth stand on in order to have the shortest possible walk to the meeting place that they pick to minimise their total combined journey?

Answer see page 141

Answer see page 141

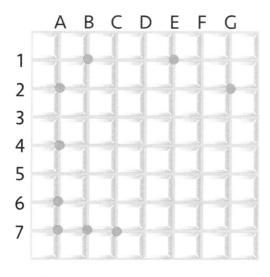

176

Five people found themselves waiting for sequential interviews at an information day for the Open University. Where did the would-be historian travel from?

The person from Norfolk worked as a estate agent, whilst the person from Rutland wanted to study philosophy, and Elvira was from Essex. The teacher, whose name was Milton, was the person immediately before the accountant. The person with red hair wanted to study sociology. The person who worked as a vet had black hair, whilst Lala had the middle spot. The resident of Hampshire had the first interview. The person with blonde hair was immediately before or after the person who wanted to study anthropology, whilst the person with black hair was immediately before or after the person wanted to study psychology. Anthony had grey hair, but the person from Cumbia had brown hair. The person from Hampshire was immediately before or after the person who worked as a life coach. Lillian was immediately before or after to a person with blonde hair.

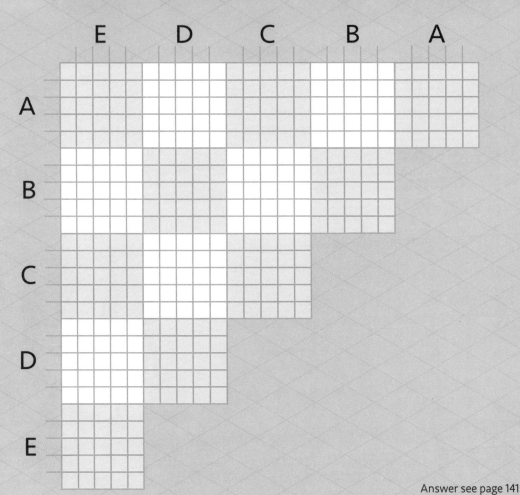

Answer see page 141

177 You are faced with three doors, two of which are wired to kill you as soon as you open them. Each door bears a sign. However, either one or none of the signs are true, you are not sure which. Which door should you open?

Sign A: This door is deadly.

Sign B: This door is safe.

Sign C: Door B is deadly.

Answer see page 141

178 The diagram below operates according to a specific logic. What should the missing square look like?

Answer see page 141

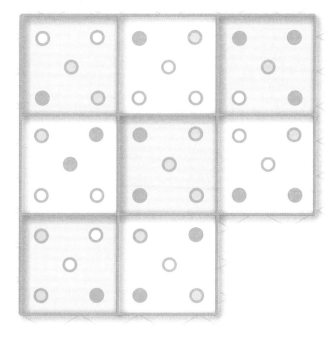

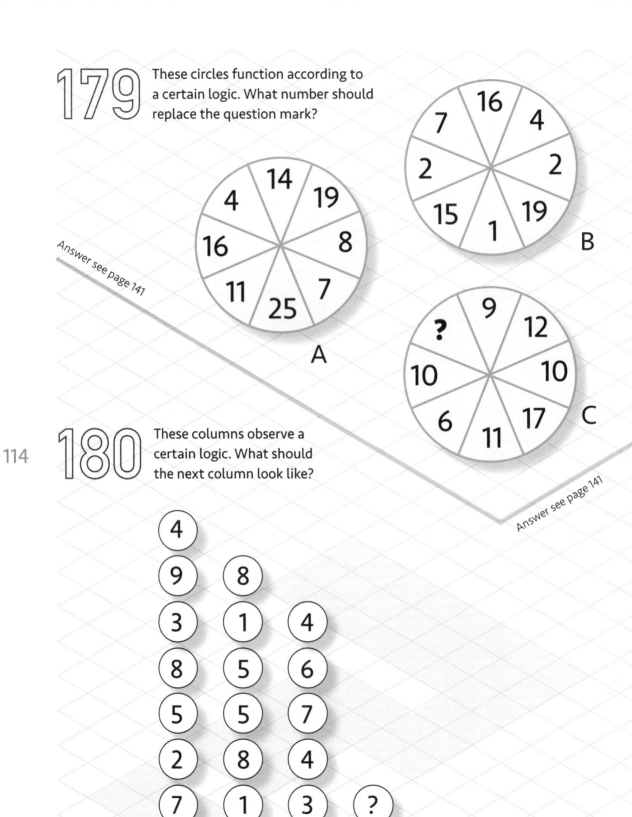

179 These circles function according to a certain logic. What number should replace the question mark?

Answer see page 141

A

B

C

Answer see page 141

180 These columns observe a certain logic. What should the next column look like?

4
9 8
3 1 4
8 5 6
5 5 7
2 8 4
7 1 3 ?

114

181

Can you uncover the logic of this grid of letters and replace the question mark with the right letter?

Answer see page 142

Answer see page 142

182

Signs – symbols in a specific position – which appear in the outer circles are transferred to the inner circle as follows: If it appears once, it is definitely transferred. If it appears twice, it is transferred if no other symbol will be transferred from that position. If it appears three times, it will be transferred if there is no sign appearing once in that position. If it appears four times, it is not transferred. In instances where signs with the same count are competeing, then from high to low, priority runs top left – top right – bottom left – bottom right. What does the inner circle look like?

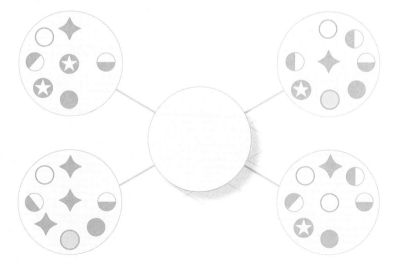

The word MAMMAL is located exactly once in the grid below, but could be horizontally, vertically or diagonally forwards or backwards. Can you locate it?

116

```
L L A L A A M A M M M A M A M
A M L M A L A M A A M M A M M
M L M A L M A M M M A A A A M
M L A A A M M L L M A A A M
A L M L L A M A M A A M M L M
M A A A L M A M A M L A A A
A M A A L M M A M M M L M L
M M M A M A L M M M A M A M M
M A L L A A M M A M M A A A A
A M L M A A M M A A M L M M M
A L M M M A A A L L L M M A
A A L M M L A M L A A M M M L
A M M M A M L M M A A M A M M
M M M M A A L A M M A A A L
L L M M A L M M A M L M A M A
```

184

A is to B as C is to
D, E, F, G or H?

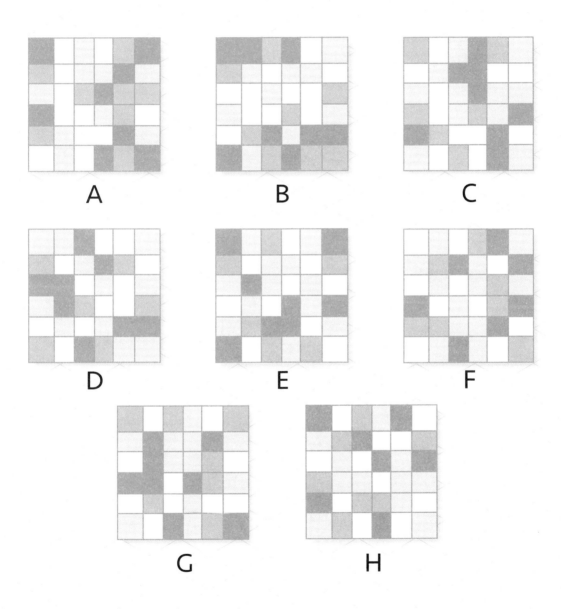

A

B

C

D

E

F

G

H

185 Imagine that there are a pair of level train tracks encircling the Earth's equator. A pair of trains are set running in opposite directions, so that they complete each a full circuit of the earth in one calendar day. Assuming that they don't fail, crash. or run out of fuel, which train's wheels will wear down first?

Answer see page 142

Answer see page 142

186 The letters and numbers in this square obey a certain logic. What letter should replace the question mark?

13	Y	T
?		8
E		O
8	P	G
	A	18

187

The following list of numbers represents uncommon colours whose letters have been encoded into the numbers needed to reproduce them on a typical phone numberpad. Can you decode them?

235 236 6
845 538 5
287 687
928 243 8
635 463
267 232 8
765 337 466

Answer see page 142

188

The following design works according to a certain logic. What number should replace the question mark?

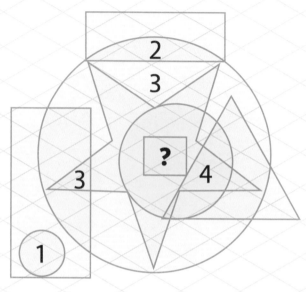

Answer see page 142

Answer see page 142

189

Jack and John want to know Jill's birthday. She informs them that it is either:

February 5,	June 17,	September 9,
March 2,	June 6,	September 13,
April 7,	July 14,	October 11,
April 16,	July 16,	October 12,
May 15,	August 14,	October 14, or
May 16,	August 15,	November 10.
May 22,	August 17,	

She then whispers the correct month to Jack, and the correct day to John, after each promises not to tell the other the information she has confided. Jack says that while he can't tell the full date of Jill's birthday, he's confident that John can't either. John replies that in that case, he knows the date. Jack then says that this means he knows it too. What is Jill's birthday?

These triangles follow a specific logic. What should replace the question mark?

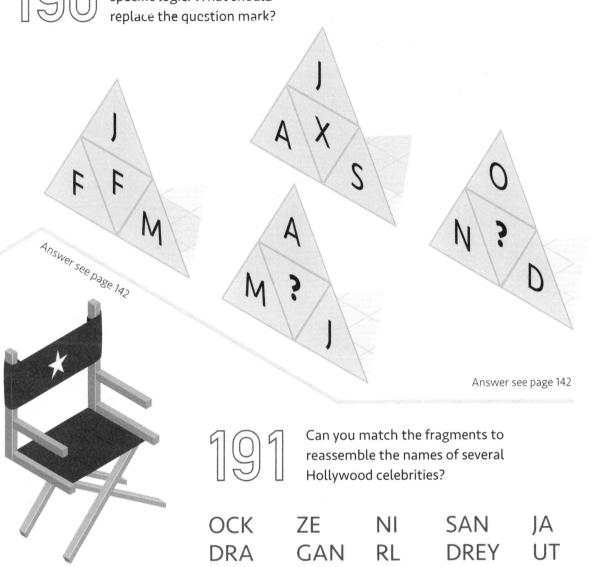

Answer see page 142

121

Answer see page 142

191

Can you match the fragments to reassemble the names of several Hollywood celebrities?

OCK	ZE	NI	SAN	JA
DRA	GAN	RL	DREY	UT
MAN	LI	MOR	SEL	ETT
SCA	DA	JO	CHOL	HANS
MI	FREE	CHA	AU	DOU
GLAS	RON	SON	CK	THE
HAS	OU	HO	EL	FF
BULL	CHAR	SON	VID	TA

192

Can you divide up this board to correctly show the 28 dominoes listed below?

4	1	0	6	6	3	3	1
5	5	0	1	1	0	4	4
5	6	2	3	6	4	6	2
0	2	2	4	3	3	0	4
0	5	2	1	6	4	3	5
0	6	5	0	1	1	1	5
2	4	5	6	2	2	3	3

0	0

0	1		1	1

0	2		1	2		2	2

0	3		1	3		2	3		3	3

| 0 | 4 | | 1 | 4 | | 2 | 4 | | 3 | 4 | | 4 | 4 |

| 0 | 5 | | 1 | 5 | | 2 | 5 | | 3 | 5 | | 4 | 5 | | 5 | 5 |

| 0 | 6 | | 1 | 6 | | 2 | 6 | | 3 | 6 | | 4 | 6 | | 5 | 6 | | 6 | 6 |

122

Answer see page 143

Answer see page 142

193

Five crooks are suspected of participating in a two-person robbery. Each gives a statement, but three of the statements are false. The three who lie are innocent. Which two are guilty?

A: B is innocent.

B: Both A and C are guilty.

C: D is guilty.

D: C is telling the truth.

E: C is innocent.

194

In the grid below, letters have been consistently replaced with the same random numbers. Can you complete the grid correctly?

1	2	3	4	5	6 D	7 H	8	9	10	11	12	13 Y
14	15	16	17	18	19	20	21	22	23	24	25	26

Answer see page 143

Examine the top three shapes.
Which of the five options A–E
continues the sequence ?

Answer see page 143

124

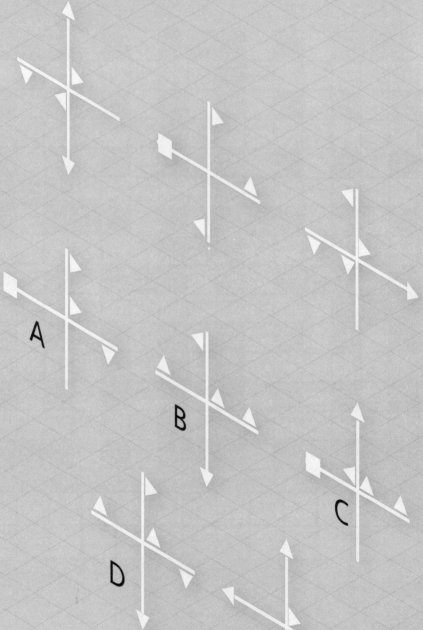

A

B

C

D

E

196 Each of the circles below contains the name of a work of literature and its author. Can you unscramble them?

A: LANDIEEHIIAIETRMHYCDETCGEDIVNO

B: TSAEABAR MDLRMEEVAYAUAFBUOTCVT

C: RCR OTIENGELEOWNONFEHLUTIYREGEERN

Answer see page 143

Answer see page 143

197 One of the squares in the 3x3 grid is incorrect. Which one?

125

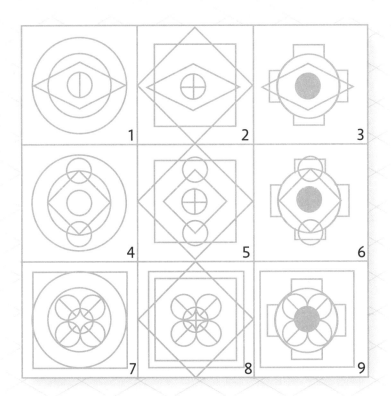

198 Jonathan was born on March 26, lives in Nashville, and is a minister. He likes Artichokes. Felicia was born August 5, lives in Galloway, and is a doctor. She likes Leeks. Magnolia was born on December 29, lives in Springfield, and is a scientist. She likes Cabbage. Steven was born on October 11th, lives in Danville, and is a lecturer. He likes Lettuce. Georgina was born on March 9, lives in Throckmorton, and is a financier. Which of the following vegetables does she like?

A. Kale
B. Peas
C. Spinach
D. Turnip
E. Brocolli

Answer see page 143

199 In this long division calculation, each digit has been consistently replaced with a letter chosen at random. Can you discover the original calculation?

Answer see page 143

200

The following tiles have been taken from a five by five square of numbers. When they have been reassembled accurately, the square will show the same five numbers reading both across and down. Can you rebuild it?

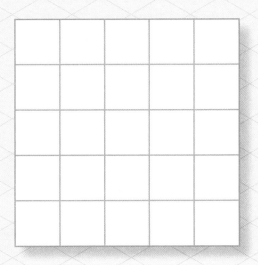

5	5	0		1		9		4		5

| 7 | 4 | 6 | | 9 | | 7 | | 3 | | 5 |

0
3
2

5	5

	1

7	6	3	5	7

Answer see page 143

201

The following grid operates according to a specific pattern. Can you fill in the blank section?

Answer see page 143

THE
ANSWERS

1

2

Minnie Driver. Angelina Jolie. Alyson Hannigan. Julia Dreyfus. Rip Torn. Mel Gibson. Matthew McConaughey. Kiefer Sutherland. Owen Wilson.

3

In step 4, the instruction does not specify that vehicles need to be moving.

4

Our solutions: a. 7–6*5/15+18 = 23. b. 9+(7*7+3)/13 = 13. c. (8*9/12+14)/5 = 4.

5

Pattern runs right to left from top left.

6

B (More specific sign must be the false one.)

7

S (Add arithmetical values of letter positions and convert total back to a letter, wrapping from Z=26 to A=27.)

8

5 (E = B).

9

A: 220 (Statement 2 is wrong). B: 260 (Statement 1 is wrong). C: 200 (Statement 3 is wrong).

10

Y.

11

0	2	8	5	4
2	3	5	7	9
8	5	6	3	4
5	7	3	0	2
4	9	4	2	3

12

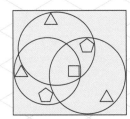

13

C4.

14

Desk 4.

15

Vermont, Kentucky, Oregon, Nebraska, Oklahoma.

16

17

17 (The terms are successive prime numbers).

18

They are not playing each other.

19

9 (= 7-2+4).

20

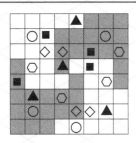

21

104 (The numbers increase by the prime numbers in sequence).

22

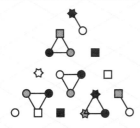

23

	6	7	4	8			9		7	1	9
	9			4		8	6	3	1		3
6	9	3	0	3	9	5	2	9		3	6	6
8		4			1		3				1
4	5	2			3	5	4	6	4	3	6	3
1		6				6		3		0		5
		5	6	9	4	2	9	5	0	3		9
4	7	5		7		7		2		9		6
9		1	8	7	0			5	6	6
0			0			3	8	2	2
8	2	1	4	6	5		1		6	6	2
	6		3		6		4		4		3
2	5	1		6	4	3	6	5	4	9	7	0

24

C (No liar could ever admit the fact).

25

26

18 (segment by segment, C = A * B).

27

2 ("Tumbler").

28

203840 / 14= 14560.

29

80%.

30

C.

31

32

B (66% vs 50%).

33

13 (Difference between H=8 and U=21).

34

A little under 1.5 billion kilometres.

35

Prague, Barcelona, Glasgow, Brisbane, Vancouver, Dubai.

36

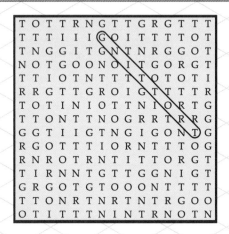

37

F (The letters represent the numbers 1-9 based on their position in the alphabet, in this instance forming a magic square which totals 15).

38

11:46.43. (Time decreases by 1:13.04, 2:26.08, 3:39.12, 4:52.16 minutes).

39

40

B.

41

6.

42

4 (Convert numbers to the letters at those positions in the alphabet. Spells out DISAPPOINTINGLY, reading top left -> bottom right through each block).

43

C.

44

1.

45

Otis (Otis, engineer, duck, Oregon. Bobbie, botanist, chocolate, Ohio. Hersh, farmer, cherries, Vermont. Margaret, doctor, bread, Louisiana. Angie, researcher, lamb, Arizona).

46

A light blue square with a white ball in the top left and black balls in the other three corners.

47

7 (The difference between bottom left and sum of other 3 corners).

48

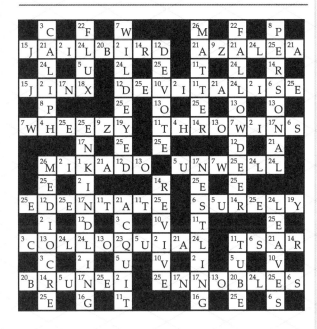

49

Stephen Poliakoff. Oscar Wilde. Johann Wolfgang von Goethe. Federico García Lorca. Lillian Hellman. George Bernard Shaw. Nikolai Gogol. Aristophanes. Christopher Marlowe. Sarah Kane.

50

9 (The small white balls are overwriting the large circle).

51

4 squared = 16.

52

85 (= 28+17+23+17).

53

The 1UR tile that's in row 4 and column 4, where 1,1 is the top left corner.

54

8pm (Total of numbers pointed at increases by 2 each time).

55

G (The others all have a functionally identical partner).

56

17 (Each ball is equal to the sum of the individual digits of the two balls to its right in the same line. The two rightmost balls in each line are that line's starting condition).

57

38 (= 5+9+7+8+9).

58

3 (Number of rectangles enclosing the value).

59

C (Triangle).

60

Y, with 0:45.20. (V=46:23, W=48:18, X=47:30, Y=45:20, Z=46:06).

61

Our solutions: a. 12+17–9+6–14=12. b. 26–10+4–17+11=14. c. –15+17+9–8+13=16.

62

A: In Search Of Lost Time, Marcel Proust. B: Finnegan's Wake, James Joyce. Don Quixote, Miguel De Cervantes.

63

D (The length of the sport is the same length as the name).

133

64

12.

65

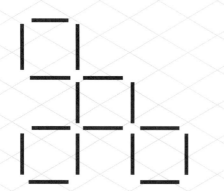

66

B.

67

9 (Each ring totals the same as its opposite number).

68

7 (= The prime numbers in ascending order, starting from 2. The two bottom points of the triangles taken as a single number are the square numbers in ascending order, and the top points are the digits counting down from 9).

69

The 1U tile that's in row 4 and column 3, where 1,1 is the top left corner.

70

W (The letters spell out the quote "Who is down needs fear no fall", starting from the question mark and running first inwards then anticlockwise around the circle.)

71

4. (Convert numbers to the letters at those positions in the alphabet. Spells out DISAPPOINTINGLY, reading top left -> bottom right through each block).

72

58.33% (7 chances out of 12).

73

17.

74

75

Anna.

76

77

F (The letters represent numbers based on their position in the alphabet, where the first column * the second = the third).

78

Pattern zig-zags up then back down, from bottom left.

79

23 (The numbers come in pairs, in the form XY and YX. 32 is unpaired).

80

Dry Martini. Manhattan. Old-fashioned. Margarita. Daiquiri. Gin Fizz. Mint Julep.

81

Infinitely (You've already used all the time up).

82

Take a second pill from the first bottle, and break all four pills in half, setting the halves carefully into two separate piles. Then take one pile today, and one pile tomorrow.

83

4	8	6	1	9
8	2	8	5	6
6	8	3	4	2
1	5	4	1	1
9	6	2	1	7

84

C (The others all have a functionally identical partner).

85

Countertop, Playpen, Antimacassar, Credenza, Sideboard, Tallboy.

86

X.

87

1 (The top left small ball is missing its horizontal stroke).

88

15 (The numbers indicate the position in the alphabet of the intial letters of the months, starting with January. J=10, F=6, M=13, A=1, etc.)

89

A.

90

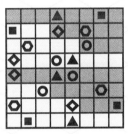

91

A: Moby Dick, Herman Melville. B: Hamlet, William Shakespeare. C: War and Peace, Leo Tolstoy.

92

412804 / 23 = 17948.

93

It should read 3 7 1 9 from top to bottom (Remove top digit, reverse).

94

C (Initial letter of the disliked location is the sixth letter of the name; and of the liked location, the fifth – she likes Inverness).

95

6 (Difference between (Top left * top right) and (bottom left * bottom right)).

96

9 (Number of sides belonging to all regular polygons, both proper and improper, enclosing the value).

97

Magdalena (Magdalena, cheese, red, geraniums. Thad, tuna, pink, azaleas. Matt, egg, purple, pansies. Hayden, ham, white, camellias. Liza, chicken, blue, delphiniums).

98

The 3D tile that's in row 2 and column 7, where 1,1 is the top left corner.

99

100

O (Words spiral in clockwise from top).

101

8.16pm (Hour increases by 1, 2, 3; minutes decreases by 12).

102

37 (Sum of arithmetic value of alphabet positions of R and S).

103

It should read 2 4 1 from top to bottom. (Add top and bottom numbers and place result downwards in next column, then work inwards).

104

D (A and C are lying).

105

W, with a total time of 1:15.06 (V=1:16.38, W=1:15:06, X=1:15:45, Y=1:19.48, Z=1:16:59).

106

A light blue square with white balls at bottom left and bottom right, and dark blue balls at top left and top right. (The squares in the middle row have been rotated 90 degrees clockwise).

107

61 (= 13+16+15+17).

108

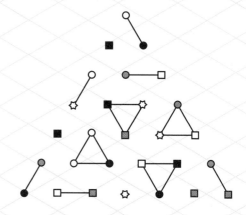

109

D (Rectangle).

110

B (Both signs are false; sign 1 cannot belong to Door A without causing a paradox).

111

35.

112

1	0	9	8	5		9	4	2		3		
8		1		2	9	3		5	1	2	0	0
7		1		4		7		3		6		
1	1	2	1	7	9	6	6		6	7	8	
2			5		6				0			
7	4	9		5	6	0	7	1		2		
	7			2		9		1	8	2	9	1
3	7	2	5	5		8		6		6		4
6		7		2	1	5	6	2	8	0	7	2
4		7			7			4				3
3	0	8	9		8	3	4		6	3	9	
8		9			9				7		8	
2	3	2		7	3	4	7	3	8	5		

113

Catherine Deneuve. Halle Berry. Jennifer Lawrence. Miley Cyrus. Sacha Baron Cohen. Denzel Washington. Peter Stormare. Rowan Atkinson.

114

C (A & C oppose. C's self-reflective statement means C either random, or statement true, but C random makes A & B paradoxical. So C is true, and B is random, and since C is true, C must be honest, leaving A as liar).

115

C.

116

5 (To see why, consider the case of just two statements. Odd numbers of statements are insoluble).

117

B.

118

04:56.27 (Sum of digits increases by three).

119

4³ = 64.

120

1113122113 (Each term is equal to the vocal enumeration of the digits in the previous term – "3"; "one 3"; "one 1, one 3"; "three 1s, one 3", etc.)

121

A (10+3+25+25+15. B=50+25+1+1+1. C=50+10+10+5+3).

122

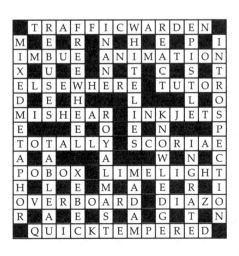

123

7463524131 (Step 6's result is not recorded).

124

3 (● = 1, ■ = 2, ▲ = 3).

125

8 (● = 2, ■ = 3, ▲ = 5).

126

Henrik Ibsen. Alexander Ostrovsky. Mikhail Bulgakov. Harold Pinter. Miguel de Cervantes. Tom Stoppard. Thornton Wilder. Pierre Corneille. John Osborne. Juan Ruiz de Alarcón.

127

128

23.

129

130

Three instances of 1, two instances of 2, three instances of 3, one instance of 4, and one instance of 5. (Five space + five digits, so total must be 10. Try all 1s and iterate to find the solution).

131

132

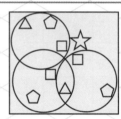

133

134

Desk 7

135

28 (Segments with even numbers in the inner and middle rings total 50).

136

Flip a coin ($\frac{1}{2}$ chance versus $\frac{5}{12}$ chance).

137

0 (D = the last digit of bc - A, treating bc as a two-digit number).

138

34 (= 5+8+5+9+7).

139

Battenberg cake, Oatmeal, Escalivada, Quorn, Corned beef, Jambalaya, Ratatouille, Jerky.

140

D.

141

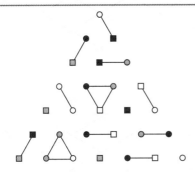

142

G.

143

I threw it straight upwards.

144

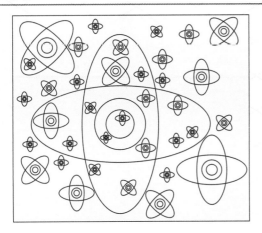

145

Our solutions: a. 4^2*3/4-8 – 4.
b. (√ 25+4)^2–(4^3) =17.
c. ((5!+5)*.5–.5)–5–((5+5)/5) = 55.

146

147

1225 (Christmas day).

148

5 (taking each wheel as a single number clockwise from 12 o'clock, C=A-B).

149

6 (=bottom right and centre, taken as a first and second digits of a single number = top * bottom left of the previous triangle).

150

9	5	9	0		5	0	3	7	5	9	3	
8				4			4		4		1	
6	3	7	2	5	1		1	2	8	7	0	
0		8		6			3					
4	1	7		9	5	8	1	6	4	6		3
		8	7	4		5		9		8		6
9	6	3		1	5	4	3	3	1	4	5	5
		7		3		7		3		8		3
3	2	5	7	0		0		5				4
4		6		1	4	8	0	2	8	5	5	8
1				4				6		5		9
0			5	3	7			3	6	3	9	7
		6	4	1	4			6				

151

152

40.

153

37 (=7+8+7+8+7).

154

D5.

155

Colonel Sun (Lieutenant Colonel Nomi, Major Capheus, Captain Will, First Lieutenant Riley, First Sergeant Kala, Sergeant Lito).

156

D.

157

Flora and Susie (Anna: mathematics, engineering, micro-electronics, Japanese. Flora: Physics, programming, micro-electronics, Japanese. Susie: mathematics, physics, programming, engineering).

158

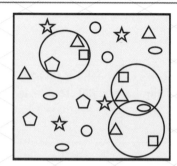

159

01:48.18 (Left to right, time alternately increases by 9h 47m 17s, then decreases by 6h 35m 23s).

160

E.

161

3 (AB = CD * E, treating AB and CD as two-digit numbers).

162

3.

163

107 (= 14+39+14+26+14).

164

C (One white ball should be yellow: the others all form part of a trio with the same numbers of balls of each colour).

165

166

In step 8, the instruction says to divide by 2. It needs to say to divide by 3.

167

3pm ("LIVE").

168

D (Pentagon).

169

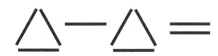

170

Ask A if the liar is to the immediate left of the random person, as they face you. If A is honest, then "Yes" means that C is random, and "No" means that B is random. If A is the liar, then "Yes" means that C is random, and "No" means that B is random. If A is random, then neither B nor C are random. Thus if you get "Yes", B is definitely non-random, and if you get "No", C is definitely non-random. Ask the identified non-random person if one of the three is a liar (or some other obvious question). If you get the answer "No", the non-random person is the liar. "If you get the answer "Yes", the non-random person the truth-teller. Ask the same person "Is A random?" to be sure of the disposition of all three.

171

X, at 46:58.12 (V=46:58.49, W=46:58.14, X=46:58.12, Y=46:58.64, Z=46:58.95).

172

$6^4 = 36^2$.

173

8 (● = 3, ▲ = 4, ■ = 6, ⬟ = 7.)

174

Jean Cocteau. Albert Camus. Yasmina Reza. Martin McDonagh. Seneca the Younger. Shelagh Delaney. Georg Büchner. Ólafur Haukur Símonarson. Pierre de Marivaux. Stephen Sondheim. Tracy Letts. Kālidāsa.

175

B4.

176

Cumbria (Int. 1, Lillian, Hampshire, vet, black hair, anthropology. Int. 2, Elvira, Essex, life coach, blonde hair, psychology. Int. 3, Lala, Norfolk, estate agent, red hair, sociology. Int. 4, Milton, Cumbria, teacher, brown hair, history. Int. 5, Anthony, Rutland, accountant, grey hair, philosophy).

177

A (B & C are mutually exclusive, so A has to be lying).

178

A light blue square with light blue balls at top left and bottom right, white balls at top right and bottom left, and a dark blue ball in the centre. (Sequence runs horizontally through the grid as WWDLDDLWLDLW).

179

9. (nC = difference between (n-2)A and (n-1)B, where (n+1) is one segment clockwise).

180

It should read 0229 from top to bottom (Treat column as a number and multiply by three, recording last digits in next column, decreasing column height by 1).

181

O (The letters spell out the word TOOTHLIKE).

182

183

```
L L A L A A M A M M M A M A M
A M L M A L A M A A M M A M M
M L M A L M A M M M A A M A M
M L A A A A M M L L M A A A M
A L M L L A M A M A A M M L M
M A A A L M A M A M L A A A A
A M A A L M M A M M M M L M L
M M M A M A L M M M A M A M M
M A L L A A M M A M M A A A A
A M L M A A M M A A M L M M M
A L M M M M A A A L L L M M A
A A L M M L A M L A A M M M L
A M M M A M L M M A A M A M M
M M M M M A A L A M M A A A L
L L M M A L M M A M L M A M A
```

184

D (Repeating pattern GWgBGgWgBWgBW goes from clockwise spiral at top left to vertical rows upwards from bottom left).

185

The one going opposite to the planet's spin (No centrifugal force lightening its weight).

186

R ("MYTHOGRAPHER").

187

Celadon, Tilleul, Atrous, Watchet, Meline, Corbeau, Solferino.

188

4 (Number of separate lines immediately surrounding the value).

189

July 16th (Jack knows her month has no unique candidate dates on the list. John then realises only July and August fit, and that he knows which it is. Jack then realises that eliminating common candidate dates in those months gives him the full answer, so it has to be July, with only one unique candidate, the 16th).

190

G (Central letter has position in alphabet equal to the sum of the positions of the months initialled around that triangle, wrapping from Z=26 to A=27).

191

Audrey Tautou. Scarlett Johansson. Sandra Bullock. Charlize Theron. David Hasselhoff. Michael Douglas. Morgan Freeman. Jack Nicholson.

192

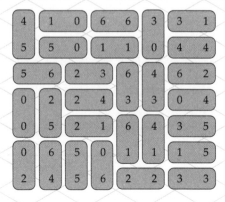

193

A & E.

194

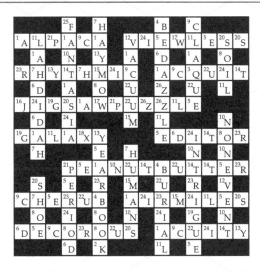

195

D.

196

The Divine Comedy, Dante Alighieri. Madame Bovary, Gustave Flaubert. Nineteen Eighty Four, George Orwell.

197

7 (The small central ball is missing).

198

B (Each person likes a vegetable that has the same initial letter as their star-sign).

199

978368 / 32 = 30574.

200

3	5	1	9	5
5	5	7	7	5
1	7	4	6	0
9	7	6	4	3
5	5	0	3	2

201

The pattern spirals inwards, clockwise, from the bottom right.

PUZZLE NOTES